BIOLOGY
The Dynamics of Life

Reviewing Vocabulary

Glencoe
McGraw-Hill

New York, New York   Columbus, Ohio   Woodland Hills, California   Peoria, Illinois

A GLENCOE PROGRAM
BIOLOGY: THE DYNAMICS OF LIFE

Student Edition

Teacher Wraparound Edition

Laboratory Manual, SE and TE

Reinforcement and Study Guide, SE and TE

Content Mastery, SE and TE

Section Focus Transparencies and Masters

Reteaching Skills Transparencies and Masters

Basic Concepts Transparencies and Masters

BioLab and MiniLab Worksheets

Concept Mapping

Chapter Assessment

Critical Thinking/Problem Solving

Spanish Resources

Tech Prep Applications

Biology Projects

Computer Test Bank Software and Manual
  WINDOWS/MACINTOSH

Lesson Plans

Block Scheduling

Inside Story Poster Package

English/Spanish Audiocassettes

MindJogger Videoquizzes

Interactive CD-ROM

Videodisc Program

Glencoe Science Professional Series:

  Exploring Environmental Issues

  Performance Assessment in the Biology Classroom

  Alternate Assessment in the Science Classroom

  Cooperative Learning in the Science Classroom

  Using the Internet in the Science Classroom

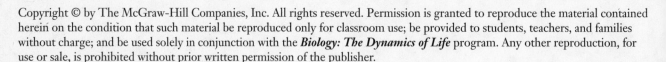

Glencoe/McGraw-Hill

A Division of The **McGraw·Hill** Companies

Send all inquiries to:
Glencoe/McGraw-Hill
8787 Orion Place
Columbus, OH 43240

ISBN 0-02-828278-7
Printed in the United States of America.
  4 5 6 7 8 9 10   047   08 07 06 05 04 03 02 01

Contents

To the Teacher iv

1 Biology: The Study of Life 1

2 Principles of Ecology 2

3 Communities and Biomes 3

4 Population Biology 4

5 Biological Diversity and Conservation . . . 5

6 The Chemistry of Life 6

7 A View of the Cell 7

8 Cellular Transport and the Cell Cycle . . . 8

9 Energy in a Cell 9

10 Mendel and Meiosis 10

11 DNA and Genes 11

12 Patterns of Heredity and
Human Genetics 12

13 Genetic Technology 13

14 The History of Life 14

15 The Theory of Evolution 15

16 Primate Evolution 16

17 Organizing Life's Diversity 17

18 Viruses and Bacteria 18

19 Protists 19

20 Fungi 20

21 What Is a Plant? 21

22 The Diversity of Plants 22

23 Plant Structure and Function 23

24 Reproduction in Plants 24

25 What Is an Animal? 25

26 Sponges, Cnidarians, Flatworms,
and Roundworms 26

27 Mollusks and Segmented Worms 27

28 Arthropods 28

29 Echinoderms and Invertebrate
Chordates 29

30 Fishes and Amphibians 30

31 Reptiles and Birds 31

32 Mammals 32

33 Animal Behavior 33

34 Protection, Support, and
Locomotion 34

35 The Digestive and Endocrine
Systems 35

36 The Nervous System 36

37 Respiration, Circulation,
and Excretion 37

38 Reproduction and Development 38

39 Immunity from Disease 39

ANSWER PAGES 40

To the Teacher

This booklet consists of the vocabulary review pages from *Content Mastery*—a resource that was developed to help English language learners and other students requiring extra help in their study of **Biology: The Dynamics of Life**. The vocabulary review pages provide students with a variety of activity formats in which to review terms and demonstrate mastery of the language of biology. These formats include matching, fill-in-the-blank, true/false, interpreting and labeling diagrams, developing tables, and a variety of puzzles. Answer pages are included at the end of this booklet.

In its entirety, the *Content Mastery* booklet provides a four-page module for each chapter and each BioDigest of **Biology: The Dynamics of Life**. In addition to the vocabulary reviews, the modules supply exercises that help students master the "big picture" of the content and assimilate concepts presented in the text. *Content Mastery* also includes a study skills section that gives students ideas on how to improve their reading and vocabulary, learn from visuals, and make and interpret idea maps.

Chapter 1 **Biology: The Study of Life,** *continued*

Content Mastery

Review the Vocabulary

adaptation (ad ap TAY shun)	theory	control
data	biology	development
energy	dependent variable	ethics
evolution (ev uh LEW shun)	environment	growth
homeostasis (hoh me o STAY sus)	experiment	independent variable
organism	hypothesis (hi PAHTH us sus)	reproduction
response	organization	scientific methods
species (SPEE sheez)	safety symbol	technology (tek NAHL uh jee)
	stimulus	

The Chapter 1 vocabulary words are listed above. Review the definitions of these words. Then draw a line to match each word in the box with its definition.

a. biology
b. ethics
c. reproduction
d. homeostasis
e. experiment

1. What you do to test a hypothesis

2. Making of offspring

3. Moral principles and values held by humans

4. Study of living things

5. Living things maintaining body functions

Use the words in the box to fill in the blanks in the sentences that follow. You will not use all the words.

response	organism	organization	control
stimulus	adaptation	technology	evolution

6. A(n) _____ has all four traits of life.

7. A(n) _____ causes living things to respond.

8. Scientific research for society's needs or problems is called _____ .

9. A(n) _____ in an experiment is used as a standard for comparison.

10. _____ is the change in a species over time.

Chapter 2 Principles of Ecology, *continued*

Review the Vocabulary

abiotic factors (ahy bi YAH tihk)	autotroph
biosphere (BI o sfeer)	biotic factors (bi YAH tihk)
commensalism (kuh MEN suh liz um)	community
decomposer	ecology (ih KAH luh jee)
ecosystem (EE khy sihs tum)	food chain
food web	habitat
heterotroph (HET uh ruh trohfs)	mutualism (MYEW chuh lih zum)
niche (NIHCH)	parasitism (PAYR uh sih tih zum)
population	scavengers
symbiosis (sihm bee OH sus)	trophic level (TROH fihk)

Fill in the blank in each sentence below with the correct word from the list above. You will not use all the words.

1. An organism's _____ is the place where it lives out its life.

2. Vultures are _____ because they eat animals that are already dead.

3. The role a species has in its environment is called its _____ .

4. The study of interactions among organisms and their environments is called _____ .

5. A _____ is a group of organisms of one species that mate with one another and live in the same place at the same time.

6. An _____ uses the energy from the sun or energy stored in chemical compounds to make its own food.

7. The portion of Earth that supports life is called the _____ .

8. A _____ is a group of populations that interact with one another.

9. An organism that feeds on other organisms is called a _____ .

10. A relationship between two organisms in which one organism benefits while the other organism is harmed is called _____ .

11. A _____ breaks down and absorbs nutrients from dead organisms.

12. The nonliving parts of an organism's environment are _____ .

Chapter 3 **Communities and Biomes,** *continued*

Content Mastery

Review the Vocabulary

Match the Chapter 3 vocabulary words in the box with the definitions below. You will not use all the words.

biome	climax community	primary succession	limiting factor
permafrost	secondary succession	intertidal zone	plankton

1. Something that stops or slows down the growth of a population _____

2. Happens after a community has been destroyed _____

3. A stable or mature community _____

4. A large group of ecosystems that have the same type of climax community _____

5. Ground that is always frozen _____

Draw a line to match each vocabulary word with its description.

a. grassland
b. succession
c. tropical rain forest
d. tundra
e. aphotic zone
f. desert
g. estuary
h. taiga
i. temperate forest
j. photic zone

6. Changes in a community over time

7. Driest biome

8. Biome in which cereal grains are grown

9. Part of the ocean where sunlight penetrates

10. Most of its trees are conifers

11. Body of water in which salt water and fresh water mix

12. Has warm weather and plenty of rainfall

13. Has no trees

14. Part of the ocean where sunlight does not penetrate

15. Most of its trees lose their leaves every year

Chapter **4** **Population Biology,** *continued*

Content Mastery

Review the Vocabulary

Use the Chapter 4 vocabulary words in the box to fill in the puzzle.

| emigration | age structure |
| demography | carrying capacity |

Across

1. proportions of a population that are at different age levels

2. study of population growth characteristics

Down

3. number of organisms of one species that an environment can support

4. movement of individuals out of a population

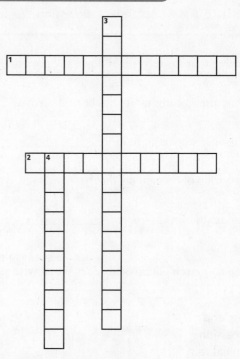

Use the vocabulary words in the box to complete the sentences.

| density-dependent factors | density-independent factors |
| exponential growth | immigration |

5. Limiting factors that affect populations more as the populations grow are

called _____ .

6. A growth rate that increases with time results in _____ .

7. Limiting factors that affect populations the same way regardless of their size are

called _____ .

8. _____ is the movement of individuals into a population.

Chapter 5 **Biological Diversity and Conservation,** *continued*

Content Mastery

Review the Vocabulary

acid precipitation	endangered species	habitat fragmentation
biodiversity	exotic species	ozone layer
captivity	extinction	reintroduction programs
conservation biology	habitat corridors	threatened species
edge effect	habitat degradation	sustainable use

The Chapter 5 vocabulary words are listed above. Review the definitions of these words. Then fill in each blank in the sentences below with the correct word from the list. You will not use all the words.

 1. A(n) _____ is a species that is declining rapidly in number.

 2. The variety of life in an area is called _____ .

 3. _____ is rain, snow, sleet, or fog that has a low pH value.

 4. Animals in zoos are in _____ .

 5. The damage to a habitat by pollution is called _____ .

 6. _____ is the disappearance of a species when its last member dies.

 7. _____ release organisms into an area where they once lived.

 8. A(n) _____ is a species whose numbers are so low that it is in danger of becoming extinct.

 9. The _____ protects organisms on Earth from ultraviolet radiation.

 10. _____ are strips of land that allow organisms to migrate from one area to another.

 11. A(n) _____ is a species that has been brought to an area where it normally does not live.

 12. _____ is the separation of a wilderness area from other wilderness areas.

Chapter 6 The Chemistry of Life, *continued*

Content Mastery

Review the Vocabulary

Some of the Chapter 6 vocabulary words are listed below. Review the definitions of these words. Then use the clues to complete the puzzle. The letters in the dark boxes will make up three words that tell you what you are studying in Chapter 6.

atom

base

carbohydrate

diffusion

enzyme

hydrogen bond

metabolism

nucleic acid

nucleotide

polar molecule

polymer

protein

solution

1. subunit of nucleic acids

2. compound used by cells to store and release energy

3. substance that forms hydroxide ions in water

4. all the chemical reactions that occur in an organism

5. mixture in which a substance dissolves into another substance

6. movement of particles from an area of higher concentration to an area of lower concentration

7. smallest particle of an element that has the characteristics of that element

8. molecule with a positive end and a negative end

9. weak bond formed between water molecules, due to their polarity

10. polymer made of amino acids that is essential to all life

11. large molecule made of many smaller molecules bonded together

12. large molecule that stores information in cells

13. protein that changes the rate of a chemical reaction

Chapter 7 A View of the Cell, *continued*

Content Mastery

Review the Vocabulary

cell	electron microscope	nucleolus
cell theory	endoplasmic reticulum	nucleus
cell wall	eukaryote (yew KER ee oht)	organelle
chlorophyll	flagella	phospholipid
chloroplast	fluid mosaic model	plasma membrane
chromatin	Golgi apparatus (GALW jee)	plastid
cilia	homeostasis	prokaryote (pro KER ee oht)
compound light	lysome	ribosome
microscope	microfilament	selective permeability
cytoplasm	microtubule	transport protein
cytoskeleton	mitochondria	vacuole

Review the Chapter 7 vocabulary words listed above. Match the words with the definitions below.

1. Cell having a nucleus and other membrane-bound organelles _____

2. Short, hairlike projections on a cell's surface that are composed of microtubules

_____

3. Fluid-filled space within the cytoplasm; temporarily stores food _____

4. Building block of both unicellular and multicellular organisms _____

5. Contains the cell's DNA and manages cell functions _____

6. Green pigment that traps light energy from the sun _____

7. The process of maintaining the cell's environment _____

8. Organelles in which food molecules are broken down to produce ATP _____

9. Creates selective permeability of plasma membrane _____

10. Rigid structure outside the plasma membrane of plant cell _____

11. Membrane sacs that receive and package proteins _____

12. Serves as a boundary between the cell and its external environment _____

13. Cell lacking a nucleus or other membrane-bound organelles _____

Chapter 8 Cellular Transport and the Cell Cycle, *continued*

Content Mastery

Review the Vocabulary

Use the Chapter 8 vocabulary words in the box below to fill in the puzzle. You will not use all of the words.

centromere

cancer

gene

centrioles

spindle

chromosomes

mitosis

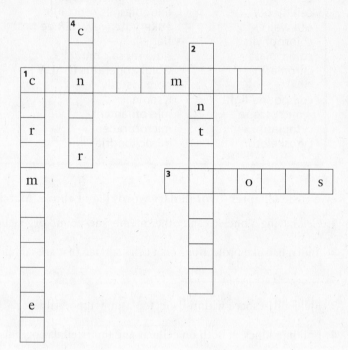

ACROSS

1. joins two sister chromatids

3. process of nuclear division

DOWN

1. structures that contain DNA

2. small, dark, cylindrical structures made of microtubules

4. result of uncontrolled cell division

Use the vocabulary words in the box below to fill in the blanks in the statements. You will not use all of the words.

isotonic solution	hypotonic solution	endocytosis	active transport
hypertonic solution	osmosis	exocytosis	passive transport

5. In a _____ , the concentration of dissolved substances is lower than the concentration inside a cell.

6. _____ is the diffusion of water through a selectively permeable membrane.

7. _____ is the expulsion of materials from a vacuole of a cell.

Chapter
9 Energy in a Cell, *continued*

Content Mastery

Review the Vocabulary

Use the Chapter 9 Vocabulary words in the box below. Review the definitions of these words. Then draw a line to match each word in the box with its definition.

---

a. light-independent reactions
b. photolysis
c. chlorophyll
d. adenosine triphosphate
e adenosine diphosphate
f. electron transport chain
g. photosynthesis
h. cellular respiration

---

1. Breaks down sugar molecules to produce ATP

2. Green pigment that absorbs sunlight

3. Splitting of water during photosynthesis to resupply electrons to chlorophyll

4. Series of proteins that pass electrons

5. Energy-storing molecule that has two phosphate groups

6. Part of photosynthesis that does not require sunlight and takes place in the stroma

7. Biological process that traps energy from the sun to make carbohydrates

8. Energy-storing molecule that has three phosphate groups

Look at each Chapter 9 vocabulary word in the box below. If the word goes with photosynthesis, write it in the table under *Photosynthesis*. If the word goes with aerobic respiration, write it under *Aerobic Respiration*. If the word goes with anaerobic processes, write it under *Anaerobic Processes*. A word may go under more than one heading.

---

citric acid cycle   light-dependent reactions   glycolysis   electron transport chain

lactic acid fermentation   alcoholic fermentation   Calvin cycle

---

Photosynthesis	Aerobic Respiration	Anaerobic Processes

Chapter 10 Mendel and Meiosis, *continued*

Review the Vocabulary

Review the definitions of the Chapter 10 vocabulary words in the box below. Then match each word with its definition by writing the letter of the word on the line provided.

a. genetics	_____ **1.** when male and female gametes unite
b. fertilization	_____ **2.** homologous chromosomes not separating properly
c. heredity	_____ **3.** passing on of traits to offspring
d. phenotype	_____ **4.** study of heredity
e. nondisjunction	_____ **5.** the appearance of an organism
f. genotype	_____ **6.** the genetic makeup of an organism

Use the Chapter 10 vocabulary words in the box below to fill in the blanks in the sentences. You will not use all the words.

diploid (DIH ployd)	homologous (huh MAHL uh gus)	genetic recombination
haploid (HAP loyd)	crossing over	gametes (GAM eets)
heterozygous	meiosis (mi OH sus)	dominant
sexual reproduction	zygote (ZI goht)	pollination

7. A cell with two of each kind of chromosome is called _____ .

8. Sperm or egg cells are _____ .

9. A cell with one of each kind of chromosome is a(n) _____ cell.

10. _____ chromosomes have genes for the same traits in the same order on both chromosomes.

11. Specialized body cells make gametes in a process that involves _____ .

12. A(n) _____ is the cell created when a sperm fertilizes an egg.

13. _____ _____ involves the production and subsequent fusion of gametes.

14. When nonsister chromatids exchange genes, the process is called _____ _____ .

15. The reassortment of genetic information, which results in variation among organisms, is called _____ _____ .

Chapter 11 **DNA and Genes,** *continued*   **Content Mastery**

Review the Vocabulary

Review the Chapter 11 vocabulary words in the box below. Then write <u>true</u> or <u>false</u> after each statement.

| double helix | nitrogen | DNA replication |

1. DNA replication produces an exact copy of a DNA molecule. _____

2. A double helix is shaped like a straight ladder. _____

3. DNA has only three different nitrogen bases. _____

Use the vocabulary words in the box below. Review the definitions of these words. Then draw a line to match each word in the box with its definition.

a. transcription
b. translation
c. transfer RNA
d. ribosomal (ri buh SOH mul) RNA
e. messenger RNA
f. codon (KOH dahn)

4. This is the set of three nitrogen bases used to make amino acids.

5. This happens when a sequence of bases in mRNA is used to make a sequence of amino acids.

6. This brings amino acids to ribosomes.

7. This carries the copied DNA code out to the cytoplasm.

8. This happens when DNA unzips and makes an RNA copy of itself.

9. This is the part of the RNA that makes up ribosomes.

Use the vocabulary words in the box below to fill in the blanks in the statements. You will not use all the words.

frameshift mutation (FRAYME shihft • mew TAY shun)	nondisjunction
chromosomal mutation	point mutation
mutagen (MYEWT uh jun)	mutation

10. A ____P_____ is a change in a single base pair in DNA.

11. Broken chromosomes are one cause of ____ch_____m_____ .

12. ____N_____ happens when homologous chromosomes fail to separate properly.

13. A ____m_____ is any agent that can cause a change in DNA.

Review the Vocabulary

autosomes	multiple alleles
carrier	pedigree
codominant alleles (koh DAH muh nunt • uh LEELZ)	polygenic inheritance
	sex chromosomes
fetus	sex-linked trait
incomplete dominance	

The Chapter 12 vocabulary words are listed above. Review the definitions of these words. Then fill in each blank in the statements below with the correct word from the list. You will not use all the words.

1. A(n) _____ shows an individual's family tree.

2. Some genes are located on sex chromosomes. A(n) _____ is a trait controlled by these genes.

3. In humans, the 22 pairs of matching homologous chromosomes are called _____ .

4. Traits controlled by more than two alleles are said to have _____ .

5. An individual with a recessive allele for an undesirable trait is called a(n) _____ .

6. In _____ , the phenotype of the heterozygote is intermediate between those of the two homozygotes.

7. _____ are chromosomes that determine the sex of an individual.

8. _____ cause the phenotypes of both homozygotes to be produced in the heterozygote.

Chapter 13 Genetic Technology, continued

Content Mastery

Review the Vocabulary

Use the Chapter 13 vocabulary words to complete the crossword puzzle. One vocabulary word has been filled in for you.

test cross
clones
gene splicing
gene therapy
genetic engineering
human genome
linkage map
plasmid
recombinant DNA
restriction enzyme
transgenic organism
vector

[Crossword puzzle grid with 6 Across answer filled in: **recombinant**]

Across

3. organisms that are genetically identical

5. the thousands of genes that make up the 46 human chromosomes

6. DNA made by connecting pieces of DNA from different sources

8. small ring of DNA

9. A mechanical or biological _____ is used to transfer DNA.

10. A test _____ involves an individual of unknown genotype and an individual of known genotype.

11. An organism that has been changed by genetic engineering is a(n) _____ organism.

Down

1. therapy that can be used to correct genetic disorders

2. enzymes used to cut DNA molecules

4. map showing the location of genes on a chromosome

5. engineering used to move genes from one organism to another

7. Gene _____ is used to reconnect pieces of DNA.

CONTENT MASTERY

Chapter 14 **The History of Life,** *continued*

Review the Vocabulary

> archaebacteria (ar kee bac TIHR ee uh)   plate tectonics
>
> biogenesis (bi oh JEN uh sus)   protocell
>
> fossil   spontaneous generation

The Chapter 14 vocabulary words are listed above. Review the definitions of these words. Then fill in the puzzle. You will not use all the words for the puzzle.

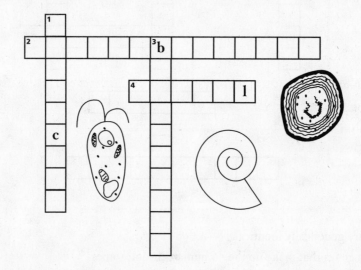

Across

  2. unicellular life forms that live with little sunlight or oxygen

  4. evidence of an organism that lived long ago

Down

  1. structure that carries out some life activities such as growth or division

  3. idea that living things come only from other living things

Fill in each blank with the correct vocabulary word.

  5. The idea that life can come from something nonliving is called _____ .

  6. The theory of _____ explains how continents move.

Review the Vocabulary

adaptive radiation	genetic equilibrium
allelic frequency	homologous structure
analogous structure	mimicry
artificial selection	natural selection
camouflage (KAM uh flahj)	punctuated equilibrium
directional selection	reproductive isolation
disruptive selection	speciation (spee shee AY shun)
embryo	stabilizing selection
gene pool	vestigial structure (veh SYTIHJ ee yul)
genetic drift	

Review the definitions of the Chapter 15 vocabulary words listed in the box. Then read the statements below. If the statement is true, write <u>true</u>. If a statement is false, replace the underlined word with another vocabulary word that will make the statement true. You will not use all the words.

1. <u>Natural selection</u> is breeding living things to select for certain traits.

_____

2. <u>Mimicry</u> enables an animal or a plant to blend with its surroundings.

_____

3. <u>Homologous structures</u> are similar structures found in groups of related organisms.

_____

4. <u>Genetic equilibrium</u> happens when allelic frequencies stay the same from generation to generation.

_____

5. The <u>allelic frequency</u> is the entire collection of genes in a population.

_____

Use the vocabulary words in the box below. Review the definitions of these words. Then draw a line to match each word in the box with its definition.

a. divergent evolution
b. geographic isolation
c. convergent evolution
d. polyploid
e. gradualism

6. When a physical barrier divides a population into groups

7. Any organism that has multiple sets of chromosomes

8. The idea that species form by gradual change over time

9. When two or more similar species become more unlike each other over time

10. When distantly related life forms develop similar traits

Chapter 16 **Primate Evolution,** *continued*

Content Mastery

Review the Vocabulary

> anthropoid (AN thruh poyd)
> australopithecine (ah stray loh pihth uh sine)
> bipedal
> Cro-Magnon
> hominid (hoh MIHN ud)
>
> Neanderthals (nee AN dur tawl)
> opposable thumb
> prehensile tail (pree HEN sul)
> primate

Use some of the Chapter 16 vocabulary words listed above to fill in the puzzle.

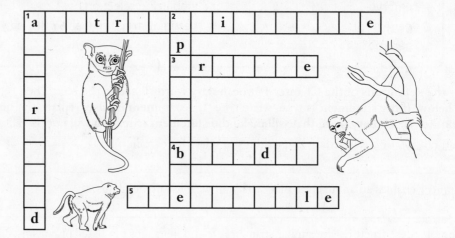

Across

1. early hominid that lived in Africa

3. group of mammals that includes lemurs, monkeys, apes, and humans

4. ability to walk upright on two legs

5. type of tail that can grasp tree branches

Down

1. subgroup of primates that includes monkeys, apes, and humans

2. type of thumb that can be used to grasp objects

Use the rest of the vocabulary words to finish the words in the sentences.

6. Ne _____ lived from 35 000 to 100 000 years ago.

7. _____ ids are humanlike primates that walk on two legs.

8. _____ o - _____ people lived in Europe 35 000 to 40 000 years ago.

80 CHAPTER 16 BIOLOGY: The Dynamics of Life

CONTENT MASTERY

Chapter 17 Organizing Life's Diversity, *continued*

Content Mastery

Review the Vocabulary

Use the Chapter 17 vocabulary words listed in the box to fill in the blanks in the sentences. You will not use all the words.

binomial nomenclature	phylogeny (fi LAW juh nee)
cladistics	protists
division	taxonomy
eubacteria	

1. The naming system called _____ gives each species a two-word name.

2. _____ is a classification system based on the derived traits of organisms.

3. _____ are prokaryotes.

4. _____ is the branch of biology that groups and names living things.

5. _____ is the history of the evolution of a species.

Draw a line to match each vocabulary word in the box with its definition.

a. family
b. order
c. genus (JEE nus)
d. phylum (FI lum)
e. class
f. kingdom

6. Group of related orders
7. Group of related genera
8. Group of related species
9. Group of related families
10. Group of related phyla
11. Group of related classes

Chapter
18 **Viruses and Bacteria,** *continued*

Content Mastery

Review the Vocabulary

Use the Chapter 18 vocabulary words in the box to fill in the puzzle.

virus (VI rus)	bacteriophage (bak TEER ee yuh fayj)	retrovirus
provirus	toxin	endospore

Across

3. virus that infects only bacteria

5. poison produced by some bacteria

6. virus whose DNA has been inserted into the host cell's chromosome

Down

1. virus that has RNA

2. tiny, nonliving particle

4. bacterium with a tough outer covering

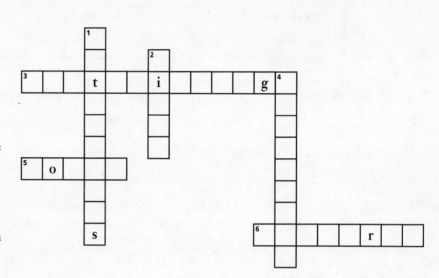

Look at each vocabulary word in the box below. If the word is related to bacteria, write it in the table under *Bacteria*. If the word is related to viruses, write it in the table under *Viruses*.

	Bacteria	Viruses
lytic cycle (LI tihk)		
lysogenic cycle (li suh JEN ihk)		
capsid		
reverse transcriptase		
obligate aerobe		
binary fission		
conjugation		
obligate anaerobe		
nitrogen fixation		

Chapter 19 Protists, *continued*

Content Mastery

Review the Vocabulary

Use the Chapter 19 vocabulary words in the box below to fill in the blanks in the sentences. You will not use all the words.

algae (AL jee)   ciliate   flagellate (FLAJ uh lut)   plasmodium (plaz MOH dee um)   pseudopodia (sew duh POH dee uh)   protozoan (proh tuh ZOH un)   sporozoan (spor uh ZOH un)

1. An animal-like protist is called a(n) _____ .

2. An animal-like protist that has flagella is called a(n) _____ .

3. A(n) _____ is a protist that produces spores.

4. Some protists use _____ to move and to capture food.

5. A(n) _____ is a protist that has cilia.

Use the vocabulary words in the box below. Review the definitions of these words. Then draw a line to match each word in the box with its definition.

a. alternation of generations   **b.** colony (KAH luh nee)   **c.** gametophyte (guh MEE tuh fite)   **d.** sporophyte (SPOR uh fite)   **e.** thallus (THAL us)

1. Haploid form of algae that produces sex cells

2. Algal body without roots, stems, or leaves

3. Group of cells that live together

4. Diploid form of algae that produces spores

5. Life cycle of algae that have a haploid stage followed by a diploid stage

Chapter
20 **Fungi,** *continued*

Content Mastery

Review the Vocabulary

Use the Chapter 20 vocabulary words in the box to fill in the puzzle. You will not use all the words.

mycorrhiza (my kuh RHY zuh)	hypha (HI fuh)
conidiophore (kuh NIH dee uh for)	sporangium (spuh RAN jee um)
haustoria (haw STOR ee uh)	mycelium (mi SEE lee um)

1. Sac or case where spores are produced _____ r ____ g _____

2. Mutualistic relationship between a fungus and a plant _____ c _____ h _____

3. Hyphae that grow into host cells without killing them _____ t _____

4. Network of filaments _____ y _____

5. Basic structural unit of fungi _____ p _____

Use the vocabulary words in the box below. Review the definitions of these words. Then draw a line to match each word in the box with its definition.

a. ascospore
b. ascus
c. basidia (buh SIH dee uh)
d. basidiospore
e. conidium (kuh NIH dee um)

6. Small sac in which sexual spores develop

7. Spore produced by basidia

8. Asexual spore in a chain of spores

9. Club-shaped hyphae

10. Spore produced in an ascus

Read the statements below. If the statement is true, write **T** on the line. If the statement is false, write **F**.

_____ **11.** A **stolon** (STOH lun) is a hypha that grows across a food source.

_____ **12.** A **zygospore** (ZI goh spor) is a fungal structure with a haploid nucleus.

_____ **13.** A **rhizoid** (RI zoyd) is a fungus that has a symbiotic relationship with green algae.

_____ **14.** **Lichens** (LI kunz) are club-shaped hyphae.

_____ **15.** A **gametangium** (gam uh TAN jee um) is a fungal structure with a haploid nucleus.

Chapter 21 **What Is a Plant?,** *continued*

Content Mastery

Review the Vocabulary

Use the Chapter 21 vocabulary words in the box to label the parts of the plant.

cuticle (KYEW tih kul)	seed
leaf	stem
root	

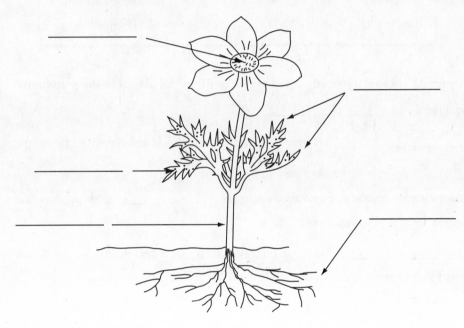

Look at the vocabulary statements below. If the statement is true, write <u>T</u> on the line. If the statement is false, write <u>F</u>.

_____ **1.** **Nonvascular plants** possess vascular tissues.

_____ **2.** A **frond** is the leaf found on ferns that vary in length from 1 cm to 500 cm.

_____ **3.** Tubelike, elongated cells through which water, food, and other materials are transported make up **vascular tissues**.

_____ **4.** **Cuticles** are scaly structures that support male or female reproductive structures.

_____ **5.** Plants that possess vascular tissues are known as **vascular plants**.

CONTENT MASTERY

Chapter
22 **The Diversity of Plants,** *continued*

Content Mastery

Review the Vocabulary

archegonium	frond (FRAWND)
antheridium	monocotyledon
cotyledon (kah tuh LEE dun)	perennial
deciduous plant (dih SIH juh wus)	prothallus
dicotyledon	rhizome (RI zohm)
fruit	sorus (SOR us)

Use the Chapter 22 vocabulary words listed above to fill in the blanks in the statements.

1. A fern leaf is called a _____ .

2. A(n) _____ has one seed leaf, leaves with parallel veins, and flower parts in multiples of three.

3. A plant that lives for several years is called a(n) _____ . It produces flowers and seeds periodically, usually once a year.

4. A(n) _____ has two seed leaves, leaves with branched veins, and flower parts in multiples of four or five.

5. A(n) _____ loses all its leaves at one time.

6. The part of the seed plant embryo that functions to store food is the _____ .

7. The thick underground stem in ferns is the _____ .

8. A(n) _____ is a male reproductive structure in which sperm are produced.

9. The spores released from a strobilus then grow to form a gametophyte, called a(n) _____ .

10. A group of sporangia on the back of a fern frond is called a(n) _____ .

11. A(n) _____ is the ripened ovary of a flower

12. The female reproductive structure in which eggs are produced is called a(n) _____ .

Chapter 23 Plant Structure and Function, *continued*

Review the Vocabulary

cortex	petiole (PET ee ohl)
epidermis	phloem (FLOH em)
guard cells	transpiration
parenchyma (puh RENG kuh muh)	tropism (TROH pih zum)
pericycle	xylem (ZI lum)

Review the Chapter 23 vocabulary words listed in the box. Then write the correct word on the line after each definition below.

1. Tissue that transports water and minerals from roots to the rest of the plant _____

2. Thin-walled cells often used for storage _____

3. Cells in leaf epidermis that control the opening and closing of stomatal pores _____

4. Leaf part that joins the leaf to the stem _____

5. A plant's response to an external stimuli that causes a growth response _____

6. Outermost layer of cells in plants _____

7. Plant tissue that helps form lateral roots _____

8. Tissue found in plant stems and roots between the epidermis and vascular core _____

9. Evaporation of water from the stomata of leaves _____

10. Tissue that transports sugar from the leaves to all parts of the plant _____

Chapter 24 **Reproduction in Plants,** *continued*

Content Mastery

Review the Vocabulary

anther	ovary
dormancy	petal
endosperm	photoperiodism
germination	short-day plant
long-day plant	stamen
micropyle (MI kruh pile)	

Review the Chapter 24 vocabulary words listed in the box. Then write the correct word on the line after each definition below.

1. Plant's response to the difference in day and night length _____

2. Flower parts that are usually brightly colored and leaflike _____

3. Process by which a seed begins to develop into a new plant _____

4. Period of seed inactivity _____

5. Tiny opening in the ovule through which sperm enter _____

6. Plant that flowers when exposed to a long night _____

7. Food-storage tissue used by developing anthophyte embryo _____

8. Female reproductive organ formed at lower end of pistil _____

9. Consists of an anther and a filament _____

10. Plant that flowers when the nights are short _____

11. Male reproductive structure that contains pollen grains _____

Chapter 25 **What Is an Animal?,** *continued*

Content Mastery

Review the Vocabulary

Circle the Chapter 25 vocabulary word in brackets that best matches each description.

1. A sponge is an example of a(n) _____ organism.

[sessile (SES sile) / dorsal / ventral / anterior]

2. hollow ball made up of a single layer of cells

[gastrula (GAS truh luh) / deuterostome (DEW tuh roh stohm) / blastula / coelom]

3. layer of cells on the outer surface of the gastrula

[ectoderm / endoderm / mesoderm / exoskeleton]

4. An earthworm is an example of a(n) _____ .

[acoelomate / pseudocoelom / protostome / gastrula]

5. Most sponges have this type of symmetry (SIH muh tree).

[radial / bilateral / asymmetry / ventral]

6. Hydras have this type of symmetry.

[radial / bilateral / asymmetry / dorsal]

7. An organism that can be divided down its length into halves that are mirror images of each other is

said to have _____ symmetry.

[radial / bilateral / ventral/ dorsal]

8. head end of a flatworm

[posterior / dorsal / ventral / anterior]

9. an animal that has three cell layers with a digestive tract but no body cavity

[pseudocoelomate / coelomate / acoelomate (uh SEE luh mayt) / protostome]

10. Humans, insects, and fishes have this type of body cavity.

[coelom (SEE lum) / pseudocoelom (sew duh SEE lum) / acoelom / gastrula]

11. An internal skeleton is called a(n) _____ .

[exoskeleton / endoskeleton / blastula / protostome (PROH tuh stohm)]

Chapter 26 Sponges, Cnidarians, Flatworms, and Roundworms, *continued*

Content Mastery

Review the Vocabulary

a. external fertilization

b. filter feeding

c. gastrovascular cavity (gas troh VAS kyuh lur)

d. hermaphrodite (hur MAF ruh dite)

e. internal fertilization

f. medusa

g. nematocyst (nuh MAT uh sihst)

h. nerve net

i. pharynx (FAYR ingks)

j. polyp (PAH lup)

k. proglottid (proh GLAH tud)

l. scolex (SKOH leks)

Write the letters of the Chapter 26 vocabulary words on the lines after the definitions. One word has been matched with its definition to help you get started.

1. Reproduction in which the eggs are fertilized inside the animal's body _____e_____

2. Reproduction in which the eggs are fertilized outside the animal's body _____

3. Conducts nerve impulses in cnidarians _____

4. Individual, repeating sections of a tapeworm _____

5. The way in which sponges get their food _____

6. Tubelike organ used by planarians to suck food into the digestive system _____

7. Structure used by cnidarians to capture or poison their prey _____

8. Individual that can produce both eggs and sperm _____

9. Stage of cnidarian life cycle in which its body is shaped like a tube _____

10. Cavity in which cnidarian digestion takes place _____

11. Head of a tapeworm _____

12. Stage of cnidarian life cycle in which its body is shaped like an umbrella _____

Chapter 27 **Mollusks and Segmented Worms,** *continued*

Content Mastery

Review the Vocabulary

Use the Chapter 27 vocabulary words to fill in the puzzle.

| closed circulatory system | gizzard | mantle |
| nephridia (ne FRIH dee uh) | open circulatory system | radula (RAJ uh luh) |

ACROSS

2. Blood moves into open spaces around an animal's organs. This is called an

   open _____ system.

5. thin membrane that protects a mollusk's organs

6. structures that remove waste from an animal's body

DOWN

1. tonguelike organ used to scrape or cut food

3. annelid organ that grinds food

4. The blood in an animal's body stays in the blood vessels. This is called

   a(n) _____ circulatory system.

Chapter 28 Arthropods, *continued*

Content Mastery

Review the Vocabulary

appendage	chelicerae (kuh LIH sur ee)
book lungs	mandible (MAN duh bul)
compound eyes	pedipalps (PED uh palps)
larva	pheromone (FAYR uh mohn)
molting	spinnerets (sih nuh RETS)
nymph (NIHMF)	spiracles (SPEER uh kulz)
pupa	tracheal tube (TRAY kee ul)
simple eye	

Many of the Chapter 28 vocabulary words are listed in the box. Review the definitions of these words. Then fill in each blank in the sentences below with the correct word.

1. A(n) _____ is an odor given off by animals.

2. The wormlike stage of an insect is the _____ .

3. A(n) _____ is a structure that grows out of an animal's body.

4. Arachnids use _____ for holding food and for sensing.

5. The biting appendages of arachnids are called _____ .

6. Spiders use _____ to spin silk into thread.

7. Spiders and their relatives use _____ to breathe.

8. A(n) _____ hatches from an egg during incomplete metamorphosis.

9. Many arthropods see with a pair of large _____ .

10. The mouthpart an arthropod uses to hold, chew, suck, or bite food is called

a(n) _____ .

Chapter 29 **Echinoderms and Invertebrates Chordates,**
continued

Content Mastery

Review the Vocabulary

Use the Chapter 29 vocabulary words in the box to fill in the puzzle.

ampulla (am POOL uh)

madreporite (MAD ruh por ite)

notochord (NOH tuh kord)

pedicellaria (ped uh suh LAYR ee uh)

ray

Across

3. disk-shaped opening in an echinoderm's body that lets water in and out

4. long, tapering arm of an echinoderm

5. round, muscular structure that squeezes water into or out of tube feet

Down

1. long, rodlike structure in all chordates

2. pincerlike appendage on an echinoderm

Find the vocabulary word in the box that matches each definition. Then write the letter of the word on the line in front of the definition.

a. dorsal hollow nerve cord

b. gill slits

c. tube feet

d. water vascular system

_____ **6.** System in echinoderms that helps them move, respire, eat, and get rid of waste

_____ **7.** Hollow, thin-walled tubes with a suction cup on the end

_____ **8.** Tube of cells surrounding a fluid-filled canal above the notochord

_____ **9.** Paired openings located behind the mouth

Chapter 30 Fishes and Amphibians, *continued*

Content Mastery

Review the Vocabulary

cartilage	ectotherm
fin	lateral line system
scale	spawning
swim bladder	vocal cords

Use three of the Chapter 30 vocabulary words listed above to fill in the blanks in the statements.

1. The _____ is a line of canals along the side of a fish that help it detect movements and find its way in the dark.

2. A(n) _____ is a gas-filled sac in bony fishes that helps them control their depth.

3. _____ are bands of tissue in the throats of frogs and mammals. These bands enable animals to make sounds.

Use the rest of the vocabulary words to fill in the puzzle.

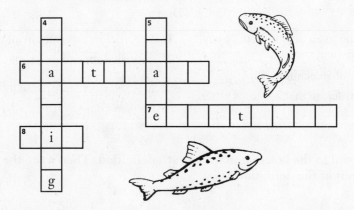

Across

6. tough, flexible material that forms the skeleton in some fishes

7. animal whose body temperature is controlled by the environment

8. fan-shaped membrane used by fishes for balance

Down

4. kind of breeding in fish and some other animals

5. one of many thin, bony plates that cover the skin of a fish

CONTENT MASTERY

REVIEWING VOCABULARY

Chapter 31 **Reptiles and Birds,** *continued*

Content Mastery

Review the Vocabulary

endotherm	amniotic egg (am nee YAH tihk)
feather	Jacobson's organ
sternum	

Use the Chapter 31 vocabulary words listed above to fill in the puzzle.

Across

3. Reptiles use their _____ organ to detect chemicals in the air.

5. animal that maintains a constant body temperature even if the temperature of its environment changes

Down

1. kind of egg that has a shell and fluid to protect the embryo

2. lightweight, modified scale that provides insulation for birds and allows them to fly

4. breastbone

Chapter
32 **Mammals,** *continued*

Content Mastery

Review the Vocabulary

Use the Chapter 32 vocabulary words in the box to fill in the blanks below.

> gestation (jes TAY shun)   mammary gland
>
> marsupial   placenta
>
> placental mammal   uterus (YEW tuh rus)

1. Muscular, hollow organ in which offspring develop _____ t _____

2. Type of mammal that carries its young inside the uterus until development is nearly complete _____ a _____ m _____

3. Time during which young mammals develop in the uterus _____ s _____

4. Organ that develops during pregnancy, provides food and oxygen to the embryo, and removes wastes _____ l _____ e _____

5. Gland in female mammals that produces milk for the young _____ m _____ a _____

6. A kangaroo is a _____ a _____ u _____

Draw a line to match each vocabulary word in the box with its definition.

> **a.** diaphragm (DI uh fram)
> **b.** gland
> **c.** monotreme (MAH nun treem)
> **d.** therapsid (thuh RAP sud)

7. Egg-laying mammal

8. Mammal-like reptile ancestor of all mammals

9. Sheet of muscle under the chest cavity that helps mammals breathe

10. Group of cells that secrete substances needed by an animal

Chapter 33 **Animal Behavior,** *continued*

Content Mastery

Review the Vocabulary

Review the definitions of the Chapter 33 vocabulary words in bold type in the statements below. If the statement is true, write <u>true</u>. If the statement is false, write <u>false</u>.

_____ **1.** An **instinct** is anything an animal does in response to a stimulus in the environment.

_____ **2.** **Innate behavior** is inherited behavior.

_____ **3.** **Courtship behavior** takes place before male and female animals mate.

_____ **4.** **Aggressive** behavior is not threatening to other animals.

_____ **5.** A **territory** is a physical space where animals breed, feed, or get shelter.

_____ **6.** The **fight-or-flight response** prepares the body for greater activity.

_____ **7.** Animals that live in very cold climates experience **estivation** (es tuh VAY shun).

_____ **8.** A 24-hour cycle of behavior is called a **circadian** (sur KAY dee un) **rhythm.**

_____ **9.** During **hibernation**, animals have a great need for oxygen and energy.

_____ **10.** A **dominance hierarchy** is a social order with several levels.

Draw a line to match each word in the box with its definition.

a. communication **b.** conditioning **c.** habituation (huh bih chuh WAY shun) **d.** imprinting **e.** insight **f.** language **g.** motivation **h.** trial-and-error learning	**11.** Internal need that causes an animal to act **12.** Occurs when an animal is given a stimulus without punishment or reward **13.** Attachment to an object during a certain time in an animal's life **14.** Kind of learning in which an animal is rewarded for a particular response **15.** kind of learning in which an animal uses its experience to respond to something new **16.** kind of learning in which an animal connects a new stimulus to a certain behavior **17.** Using symbols to represent ideas **18.** Sharing of information that results in a change of behavior

Chapter 34 **Protection, Support, and Locomotion,** *continued*

Content Mastery

Review the Vocabulary

Use the Chapter 34 vocabulary words in the box to complete the spelling of the word defined to the left. You will not use all the words.

> dermis (DUR mus)   epidermis   hair follicle
> keratin (KAYR uh tun)   melanin (MEL uh nun)   myosin (MI uh sun)

1. thin, outer layer of skin _____ d _____

2. protein in dead epidermal cells _____ at _____

3. cell pigment that colors the skin and protects it from sun damage _____ el _____

4. thick, inner layer of skin _____ is _____

5. small cavity in the dermis that grows hair _h_____ f_____

Review the definitions of the underlined vocabulary words in the statements below. If the statement is true, write <u>true</u>. If the statement is false, replace the underlined word with another vocabulary word that will make the statement true.

6. The <u>axial skeleton</u> includes the bones of the arms and legs. _____

7. A knee is an example of a <u>joint</u>. _____

8. A <u>ligament</u> is a thick band of tissue that attaches muscles to bone. _____

9. <u>Bursae</u> (BUR sigh) are fluid-filled sacs in joints. _____

10. A potential bone cell is called an <u>osteoblast</u> (AH stee uh blast). _____

11. <u>Compact bone</u> has many holes and spaces. _____

12. <u>Marrow</u> is the soft tissue inside of bones. _____

13. <u>Smooth muscle</u> is found in the heart. _____

14. <u>Skeletal muscle</u> is attached to bones and moves the skeleton. _____

15. <u>Involuntary muscle</u> contracts when you try to contract it. _____

16. A small fiber that makes up larger muscle fibers is called a <u>myofibril</u> (mi yuh FI brul).

_____

17. Thick filaments in myofibrils are made of the protein <u>actin</u>. _____

18. Each section of a myofibril is called a <u>sarcomere</u> (SAR koh meer). _____

19. The <u>sliding filament theory</u> states that actin filaments slide together during muscle contraction.

_____

Chapter 35 The Digestive and Endocrine Systems, *continued*   **Content Mastery**

Review the Vocabulary

amylase (AM uh lays)	pancreas (PANG kree us)
bile	peristalsis (payr uh STAWL sus)
pituitary	small intestine
endocrine	stomach
gallbladder	villus (VIH lus)
negative feedback	vitamin (VI tuh mun)

Use the Chapter 35 vocabulary words in the box to fill in the blanks in the sentences.

1. The pouchlike, muscular organ that secretes acids and digestive enzymes is the _____ .

2. _____ is a chemical produced by the liver that helps break down fats.

3. The endocrine system is regulated by a _____ system.

4. _____ is a digestive enzyme that breaks starches into sugars.

5. The _____ gland controls many other glands of the endocrine system.

6. _____ is a wave of muscular contractions that moves food through the digestive system.

7. The organ that stores bile is the _____ .

8. A _____ is a fingerlike projection in the lining of the small intestine.

9. The gland that produces both hormones and digestive enzymes is the _____ .

10. Digestion is completed in the organ called the _____ .

11. A _____ is an organic substance that regulates body processes.

12. _____ glands release hormones directly into the bloodstream.

Chapter
36 **The Nervous System,** *continued*

Content Mastery

Review the Vocabulary

addiction	nervous system	cerebellum
cerebrum	cochlea	retina
neuron (NEW rahn)	reflex	taste bud
rods	withdrawal	synapse (SIH naps)

Use the Chapter 36 vocabulary words listed above to complete the puzzle. First, write the correct word on the line after each definition. Then find the same word in the letter grid and circle it. Words may be written on horizontal, vertical, or diagonal lines.

```
f  r  a  x  e  d  h  l  u  c  e  n
c  e  r  e  b  e  l  l  u  m  t  e
e  w  i  t  h  d  r  a  w  a  l  r
r  n  l  d  j  h  e  d  m  l  c  v
e  e  g  f  i  o  f  d  r  k  o  o
b  u  t  e  e  e  l  i  h  n  c  u
r  r  u  i  e  e  e  c  t  g  h  s
u  o  e  m  n  e  x  t  q  l  l  s
m  n  s  h  d  a  s  i  a  j  e  y
m  a  c  w  v  e  r  o  d  s  a  s
r  g  s  y  h  e  b  n  s  d  s  t
t  a  s  t  e  b  u  d  f  a  e  e
w  f  s  a  s  y  n  a  p  s  e  m
a  d  e  b  n  l  g  i  w  n  e  q
```

1. Psychological or physiological drug
   dependence _____

2. Layer of the eye containing rods and
   cones _____

3. Body's control center
   _____

4. Taste receptor on tongue
   _____

5. Portion of brain that maintains balance
   and muscle coordination _____

6. Psychological or physiological illness resulting from cessation of drug use _____

7. Largest portion of the brain _____

8. Place where neurons meet _____

9. Fluid-filled structure of the ear in which sound vibrations are converted into nerve
   impulses _____

10. Light receptors in the retina responsible for vision in low light _____

11. Basic structural and functional unit in the nervous system _____

12. Rapid, automatic response to a stimulus _____

Chapter 37 **Respiration, Circulation, and Excretion,** *continued*   **Content Mastery**

Review the Vocabulary

> alveoli (al VEE uh li)   nephron (NE frawn)
> aorta   plasma
> artery   pulse
> atrium   ureter (YUR uh tur)
> hemoglobin (HEE muh gloh bun)   vein
> kidneys

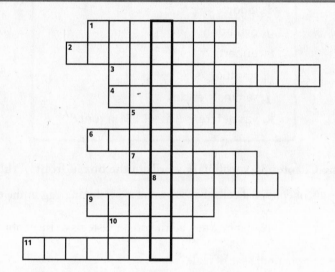

Review the definitions of the Chapter 37 vocabulary words listed above. Then use the clues to complete the puzzle. The letters in the dark boxes will make up a word that means the process by which the body balances nutrients and other things it needs for life.

1. filtering unit of the kidney

2. tiny, thin-walled sacs in the lungs

3. iron-containing molecule of red blood cells

4. tube that transports urine from each kidney to the urinary bladder

5. largest blood vessel in the human body

6. rhythmic surge of blood through an artery

7. thin-walled upper chambers of the heart

8. thick-walled blood vessel that transports blood away from the heart

9. fluid portion of the blood

10. large blood vessel that returns blood from the tissues back to the heart

11. pair of organs that filter waste from blood

Content Mastery

Review the Vocabulary

> **a.** first trimester
>
> **b.** cervix
>
> **c.** epididymis (ep uh DIHD uh mus)
>
> **d.** follicle (FAH lih kul)
>
> **e.** implantation
>
> **f.** labor
>
> **g.** ovulation
>
> **h.** puberty
>
> **i.** scrotum
>
> **j.** seminal vesicles
>
> **k.** vas deferens (vas • DEF uh runtz)

Write the letter of the Chapter 38 vocabulary words in the box in front of their definitions.

_____ **1.** Group of epithelial cells that surround a developing egg in the ovary

_____ **2.** First part of pregnancy when all the organ systems of the embryo begin to form

_____ **3.** Testes-containing sac of males

_____ **4.** Lower end of the uterus that opens into the vagina

_____ **5.** Growth stage that occurs in both males and females, characterized by the development of secondary sex characteristics

_____ **6.** Single-coiled tube in which sperm complete maturation

_____ **7.** Duct through which sperm move from the epididymis toward the urethra

_____ **8.** Process in which the follicle ruptures to release the egg from the ovary

_____ **9.** Attachment of the fertilized egg to the uterine lining

_____ **10.** Physical and psychological changes that the mother experiences during birth

_____ **11.** Paired glands at the base of the urinary bladder that produce fluid to nourish sperm

CONTENT MASTERY

REVIEWING VOCABULARY

Chapter 39 **Immunity from Disease,** *continued*

Review the Vocabulary

antibiotic	Koch's postulates	pathogen (PATH uh jun)
B cell	(KAHKS • PAHS chuh lutz)	phagocyte (FAG uh site)
interferon	lymph (LIHMF)	pus
endemic disease	lymph node	T cell
epidemic	lymphocyte	tissue fluid
immunity	(LIHMF uh site)	vaccine (vak SEEN)
(ihm YEW nut ee)	macrophage	virus
infectious disease	(MAK ruh fayj)	

For each statement below, circle the Chapter 39 vocabulary word inside the brackets that best completes the statement. You will not use every word.

1. Diseases are caused by the presence of [oxygen / antibiotics / a pathogen / alleles] in the body.

2. During a(n) [antibiotic / epidemic / genetic disorder / abnormality], many people have the same disease at the same time.

3. Penicillin is an example of a(n) [antibiotic / pathogen / endemic disease / lymphocyte].

4. The fluid in the lymphatic system is called [pus / blood / salt water / lymph].

5. A [lymphocyte / virus / phagocyte / macrophage] is *not* a white blood cell that protects the body against foreign substances.

6. The [B cell / C cell / D cell / F cell] is a type of lymphocyte.

7. [Pus / Skin / Mucus / A vaccine] can cause immunity to a disease.

8. Chicken pox, tetanus, tuberculosis, and AIDS are all [reproductive disorders / genetic disorders / infectious diseases / environmental diseases].

9. A disease that is continually present in the population is called a(n) [endemic disease / epidemic / plague / abnormality].

10. Lymph is filtered in the [lymph nodes / heart / brain / stomach].

11. When [calcium / carbon dioxide / blood / tissue fluid] enters the lymphatic vessels, it is called lymph.

12. The collection of dead white blood cells and different body fluids that are found around an infected area is called [an antibiotic / pus / complement / a vaccine].

Chapter 2 — Principles of Ecology, *continued*

Review the Vocabulary

abiotic factors (ahy bi YAH tihk)
biosphere (BI o sfeer)
commensalism (kuh MEN suh liz um)
decomposer
ecosystem (EE khy sihs tum)
food web
heterotroph (HET uh ruh trohfs)
niche (NIHCH)
population
symbiosis (sihm bee OH sus)

autotroph
biotic factors (bi YAH tihk)
community
ecology (ih KAH luh jee)
food chain
habitat
mutualism (MYEW chuh lih zum)
parasitism (PAYR uh sih tih zum)
scavengers
trophic level (TROH fihk)

Fill in the blank in each sentence below with the correct word from the list above. You will not use all the words.

1. An organism's _____**habitat**_____ is the place where it lives out its life.

2. Vultures are _____**scavengers**_____ because they eat animals that are already dead.

3. The role a species has in its environment is called its _____**niche**_____.

4. The study of interactions among organisms and their environments is called _____**ecology**_____.

5. A _____**population**_____ is a group of organisms of one species that mate with one another and live in the same place at the same time.

6. An _____**autotroph**_____ uses the energy from the sun or energy stored in chemical compounds to make its own food.

7. The portion of Earth that supports life is called the _____**biosphere**_____.

8. A _____**community**_____ is a group of populations that interact with one another.

9. An organism that feeds on other organisms is called a _____**heterotroph**_____.

10. A relationship between two organisms in which one organism benefits while the other organism is harmed is called _____**parasitism**_____.

11. A _____**decomposer**_____ breaks down and absorbs nutrients from dead organisms.

12. The nonliving parts of an organism's environment are _____**abiotic factors**_____.

Chapter 1 — Biology: The Study of Life, *continued*

Review the Vocabulary

adaptation (ad ap TAY shun)
data
energy
evolution (ev uh LEW shun)
homeostasis (hoh me o STAY sus)
organism
response
species (SPEE sheez)

theory
biology
dependent variable
environment
experiment
hypothesis (hi PAHTH us sus)
organization
safety symbol
stimulus

control
development
ethics
growth
independent variable
reproduction
scientific methods
technology (tek NAHL uh jee)

The Chapter 1 vocabulary words are listed above. Review the definitions of these words. Then draw a line to match each word in the box with its definition.

a. biology
b. ethics
c. reproduction
d. homeostasis
e. experiment

1. What you do to test a hypothesis
2. Making of offspring
3. Moral principles and values held by humans
4. Study of living things
5. Living things maintaining body functions

Use the words in the box to fill in the blanks in the sentences that follow. You will not use all the words.

response   organism   organization   control
stimulus   adaptation   technology   evolution

6. A(n) _____**organism**_____ has all four traits of life.

7. A(n) _____**stimulus**_____ causes living things to respond.

8. Scientific research for society's needs or problems is called _____**technology**_____.

9. A(n) _____**control**_____ in an experiment is used as a standard for comparison.

10. _____**Evolution**_____ is the change in a species over time.

Chapter 3 — Communities and Biomes, *continued*

Review the Vocabulary

Match the Chapter 3 vocabulary words in the box with the definitions below. You will not use all the words.

| biome | climax community | primary succession | limiting factor |
| permafrost | secondary succession | intertidal zone | plankton |

1. Something that stops or slows down the growth of a population **limiting factor**

2. Happens after a community has been destroyed **secondary succession**

3. A stable or mature community **climax community**

4. A large group of ecosystems that have the same type of climax community **biome**

5. Ground that is always frozen **permafrost**

Draw a line to match each vocabulary word with its description.

a. grassland
b. succession
c. tropical rain forest
d. tundra
e. aphotic zone
f. desert
g. estuary
h. taiga
i. temperate forest
j. photic zone

6. Changes in a community over time
7. Driest biome
8. Biome in which cereal grains are grown
9. Part of the ocean where sunlight penetrates
10. Most of its trees are conifers
11. Body of water in which salt water and fresh water mix
12. Has warm weather and plenty of rainfall
13. Has no trees
14. Part of the ocean where sunlight does not penetrate
15. Most of its trees lose their leaves every year

Chapter 4 — Population Biology, *continued*

Review the Vocabulary

Use the Chapter 4 vocabulary words in the box to fill in the puzzle.

| emigration | age structure |
| demography | carrying capacity |

Across

1. proportions of a population that are at different age levels
2. study of population growth characteristics

Down

3. number of organisms of one species that an environment can support
4. movement of individuals out of a population

Crossword answers:
1 across: a g e s t r u c t u r e
3 down: c a r r y i n g (carrying capacity)
2 across/down: d e m o g r a p h y
4 down: e m i g r a t i o n

Use the vocabulary words in the box to complete the sentences.

| density-dependent factors | density-independent factors |
| exponential growth | immigration |

5. Limiting factors that affect populations more as the populations grow are called **density-dependent factors** .

6. A growth rate that increases with time results in **exponential growth** .

7. Limiting factors that affect populations the same way regardless of their size are called **density-independent factors** .

8. **Immigration** is the movement of individuals into a population.

Chapter 6 — The Chemistry of Life, *continued*

Review the Vocabulary

Some of the Chapter 6 vocabulary words are listed below. Review the definitions of these words. Then use the clues to complete the puzzle. The letters in the dark boxes will make up three words that tell you what you are studying in Chapter 6.

atom
base
carbohydrate
diffusion
enzyme
hydrogen bond
metabolism
nucleic acid
nucleotide
polar molecule
polymer
protein
solution

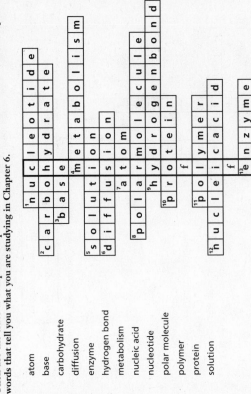

1. subunit of nucleic acids
2. compound used by cells to store and release energy
3. substance that forms hydroxide ions in water
4. all the chemical reactions that occur in an organism
5. mixture in which a substance dissolves into another substance
6. movement of particles from an area of higher concentration to an area of lower concentration
7. smallest particle of an element that has the characteristics of that element
8. molecule with a positive end and a negative end
9. weak bond formed between water molecules, due to their polarity
10. polymer made of amino acids that is essential to all life
11. large molecule made of many smaller molecules bonded together
12. large molecule that stores information in cells
13. protein that changes the rate of a chemical reaction

Chapter 5 — Biological Diversity and Conservation, *continued*

Review the Vocabulary

acid precipitation
biodiversity
captivity
conservation biology
edge effect
endangered species
exotic species
extinction
habitat corridors
habitat degradation
habitat fragmentation
ozone layer
reintroduction programs
threatened species
sustainable use

The Chapter 5 vocabulary words are listed above. Review the definitions of these words. Then fill in each blank in the sentences below with the correct word from the list. You will not use all the words.

1. A(n) __threatened species__ is a species that is declining rapidly in number.

2. The variety of life in an area is called __biodiversity__.

3. __Acid precipitation__ is rain, snow, sleet, or fog that has a low pH value.

4. Animals in zoos are in __captivity__.

5. The damage to a habitat by pollution is called __habitat degradation__.

6. __Extinction__ is the disappearance of a species when its last member dies.

7. __Reintroduction programs__ release organisms into an area where they once lived.

8. A(n) __endangered species__ is a species whose numbers are so low that it is in danger of becoming extinct.

9. The __ozone layer__ protects organisms on Earth from ultraviolet radiation.

10. __Habitat corridors__ are strips of land that allow organisms to migrate from one area to another.

11. A(n) __exotic species__ is a species that has been brought to an area where it normally does not live.

12. __Habitat fragmentation__ is the separation of a wilderness area from other wilderness areas.

Chapter 7 — A View of the Cell, *continued*

Review the Vocabulary

cell	electron microscope	nucleolus
cell theory	endoplasmic reticulum	nucleus
cell wall	eukaryote (yew KER ee oht)	organelle
chlorophyll	flagella	phospholipid
chloroplast	fluid mosaic model	plasma membrane
chromatin	Golgi apparatus (GALW jee)	plastid
cilia	homeostasis	prokaryote (pro KER ee oht)
compound light	lysome	ribosome
microscope	microfilament	selective permeability
cytoplasm	microtubule	transport protein
cytoskeleton	mitochondria	vacuole

Review the Chapter 7 vocabulary words listed above. Match the words with the definitions below.

1. Cell having a nucleus and other membrane-bound organelles ___**eukaryote**___

2. Short, hairlike projections on a cell's surface that are composed of microtubules
___**cilia**___

3. Fluid-filled space within the cytoplasm; temporarily stores food ___**vacuole**___

4. Building block of both unicellular and multicellular organisms ___**cell**___

5. Contains the cell's DNA and manages cell functions ___**nucleus**___

6. Green pigment that traps light energy from the sun ___**chlorophyll**___

7. The process of maintaining the cell's environment ___**homeostasis**___

8. Organelles in which food molecules are broken down to produce ATP ___**mitochondria**___

9. Creates selective permeability of plasma membrane ___**transport protein**___

10. Rigid structure outside the plasma membrane of plant cell ___**cell wall**___

11. Membrane sacs that receive and package proteins ___**Golgi apparatus**___

12. Serves as a boundary between the cell and its external environment ___**plasma membrane**___

13. Cell lacking a nucleus or other membrane-bound organelles ___**prokaryote**___

CONTENT MASTERY

Chapter 8 — Cellular Transport and the Cell Cycle, *continued*

Review the Vocabulary

Use the Chapter 8 vocabulary words in the box below to fill in the puzzle. You will not use all of the words.

centromere
cancer
gene
centrioles
spindle
chromosomes
mitosis

ACROSS

1. joins two sister chromatids

3. process of nuclear division

DOWN

1. structures that contain DNA

2. small, dark, cylindrical structures made of microtubules

4. result of uncontrolled cell division

Use the vocabulary words in the box below to fill in the blanks in the statements. You will not use all of the words.

isotonic solution	hypotonic solution	endocytosis	active transport
hypertonic solution	osmosis	exocytosis	passive transport

5. In a ___**hypotonic solution**___, the concentration of dissolved substances is lower than the concentration inside a cell.

6. ___**Osmosis**___ is the diffusion of water through a selectively permeable membrane.

7. ___**Exocytosis**___ is the expulsion of materials from a vacuole of a cell.

CONTENT MASTERY   CHAPTER 8   BIOLOGY: The Dynamics of Life   **39**

Chapter 9 — Energy in a Cell, *continued*

Content Mastery

Review the Vocabulary

Use the Chapter 9 Vocabulary words in the box below. Review the definitions of these words. Then draw a line to match each word in the box with its definition.

a. light-independent reactions
b. photolysis
c. chlorophyll
d. adenosine triphosphate
e. adenosine diphosphate
f. electron transport chain
g. photosynthesis
h. cellular respiration

1. Breaks down sugar molecules to produce ATP
2. Green pigment that absorbs sunlight
3. Splitting of water during photosynthesis to resupply electrons to chlorophyll
4. Series of proteins that pass electrons
5. Energy-storing molecule that has two phosphate groups
6. Part of photosynthesis that does not require sunlight and takes place in the stroma
7. Biological process that traps energy from the sun to make carbohydrates
8. Energy-storing molecule that has three phosphate groups

Look at each Chapter 9 vocabulary word in the box below. If the word goes with photosynthesis, write it in the table under *Photosynthesis*. If the word goes with aerobic respiration, write it under *Aerobic Respiration*. If the word goes with anaerobic processes, write it under *Anaerobic Processes*. A word may go under more than one heading.

citric acid cycle   light-dependent reactions   glycolysis   electron transport chain
lactic acid fermentation   alcoholic fermentation   Calvin cycle

Photosynthesis	Aerobic Respiration	Anaerobic Processes
light-dependent reactions	citric acid cycle	glycolysis
Calvin cycle	glycolysis	lactic acid fermentation
electron transport chain	electron transport chain	alcoholic fermentation

---

Chapter 10 — Mendel and Meiosis, *continued*

Content Mastery

Review the Vocabulary

Review the definitions of the Chapter 10 vocabulary words in the box below. Then match each word with its definition by writing the letter of the word on the line provided.

a. genetics
b. fertilization
c. heredity
d. phenotype
e. nondisjunction
f. genotype

b 1. when male and female gametes unite
e 2. homologous chromosomes not separating properly
c 3. passing on of traits to offspring
a 4. study of heredity
d 5. the appearance of an organism
f 6. the genetic makeup of an organism

Use the Chapter 10 vocabulary words in the box below to fill in the blanks in the sentences. You will not use all the words.

diploid (DIH ployd)   homologous (huh MAHL uh gus)   genetic recombination
haploid (HAP loyd)   crossing over   gametes (GAM eets)
heterozygous   meiosis (mi OH sus)   dominant
sexual reproduction   zygote (ZI goht)   pollination

7. A cell with two of each kind of chromosome is called **diploid**.
8. Sperm or egg cells are **gametes**.
9. A cell with one of each kind of chromosome is a(n) **haploid** cell.
10. **Homologous** chromosomes have genes for the same traits in the same order on both chromosomes.
11. Specialized body cells make gametes in a process that involves **meiosis**.
12. A(n) **zygote** is the cell created when a sperm fertilizes an egg.
13. **Sexual** **reproduction** involves the production and subsequent fusion of gametes.
14. When nonsister chromatids exchange genes, the process is called **crossing** **over**.
15. The reassortment of genetic information, which results in variation among organisms, is called **genetic** **recombination**.

Chapter 12 · Patterns of Heredity and Human Genetics, *continued*

Review the Vocabulary

autosomes	multiple alleles
carrier	pedigree
codominant alleles (koh DAH muh nunt • uh LEELZ)	polygenic inheritance
	sex chromosomes
fetus	sex-linked trait
incomplete dominance	

The Chapter 12 vocabulary words are listed above. **Review the definitions of these words. Then fill in each blank in the statements below with the correct word from the list. You will not use all the words.**

1. A(n) __pedigree__ shows an individual's family tree.

2. Some genes are located on sex chromosomes. A(n) __sex-linked trait__ is a trait controlled by these genes.

3. In humans, the 22 pairs of matching homologous chromosomes are called __autosomes__.

4. Traits controlled by more than two alleles are said to have __multiple alleles__.

5. An individual with a recessive allele for an undesirable trait is called a(n) __carrier__.

6. In __incomplete dominance__, the phenotype of the heterozygote is intermediate between those of the two homozygotes.

7. __Sex chromosomes__ are chromosomes that determine the sex of an individual.

8. __Codominant alleles__ cause the phenotypes of both homozygotes to be produced in the heterozygote.

Chapter 11 · DNA and Genes, *continued*

Review the Vocabulary

Review the Chapter 11 vocabulary words in the box below. **Then write true or false after each statement.**

double helix	nitrogen	DNA replication

1. DNA replication produces an exact copy of a DNA molecule. ___true___

2. A double helix is shaped like a straight ladder. ___false___

3. DNA has only three different nitrogen bases. ___false___

Use the vocabulary words in the box below. Review the definitions of these words. Then draw a line to match each word in the box with its definition.

a. transcription
b. translation
c. transfer RNA
d. ribosomal (ri buh SOH muh) RNA
e. messenger RNA
f. codon (KOH dahn)

4. This is the set of three nitrogen bases used to make amino acids.

5. This happens when a sequence of bases in mRNA is used to make a sequence of amino acids.

6. This brings amino acids to ribosomes.

7. This carries the copied DNA code out to the cytoplasm.

8. This happens when DNA unzips and makes an RNA copy of itself.

9. This is the part of the RNA that makes up ribosomes.

Use the vocabulary words in the box below to fill in the blanks in the statements. You will not use all the words.

frameshift mutation (FRAYME shihft • mew TAY shun)	nondisjunction
	point mutation
chromosomal mutation	mutation
mutagen (MYEWT uh jun)	

10. A __point mutation__ is a change in a single base pair in DNA.

11. Broken chromosomes are one cause of __chromosomal mutation__.

12. __Nondisjunction__ happens when homologous chromosomes fail to separate properly.

13. A __mutagen__ is any agent that can cause a change in DNA.

Chapter 13 Genetic Technology, *continued*

Review the Vocabulary

Use the Chapter 13 vocabulary words to complete the crossword puzzle. One vocabulary word has been filled in for you.

test cross
clones
gene splicing
gene therapy
genetic engineering
human genome
linkage map
plasmid
recombinant DNA
restriction enzyme
transgenic organism
vector

Across

3. organisms that are genetically identical

5. the thousands of genes that make up the 46 human chromosomes

6. DNA made by connecting pieces of DNA from different sources

8. small ring of DNA

9. A mechanical or biological _____ is used to transfer DNA.

10. A test _____ involves an individual of unknown genotype and an individual of known genotype.

11. An organism that has been changed by genetic engineering is a(n) _____ organism.

Down

1. therapy that can be used to correct genetic disorders

2. enzymes used to cut DNA molecules

4. map showing the location of genes on a chromosome

5. engineering used to move genes from one organism to another

7. Gene _____ is used to reconnect pieces of DNA.

Chapter 14 The History of Life, *continued*

Review the Vocabulary

archaebacteria (ar kee bac TIHR ee uh)
biogenesis (bi oh JEN uh sus)
fossil
plate tectonics
protocell
spontaneous generation

The Chapter 14 vocabulary words are listed above. Review the definitions of these words. Then fill in the puzzle. You will not use all the words for the puzzle.

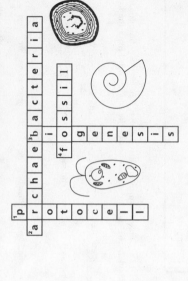

Across

2. unicellular life forms that live with little sunlight or oxygen

4. evidence of an organism that lived long ago

Down

1. structure that carries out some life activities such as growth or division

3. idea that living things come only from other living things

Fill in each blank with the correct vocabulary word.

5. The idea that life can come from something nonliving is called **spontaneous generation** .

6. The theory of **plate tectonics** explains how continents move.

Chapter 15 **The Theory of Evolution,** *continued*

Review the Vocabulary

adaptive radiation	genetic equilibrium
allelic frequency	homologous structure
analogous structure	mimicry
artificial selection	natural selection
camouflage (KAM uh flahj)	punctuated equilibrium
directional selection	reproductive isolation
disruptive selection	speciation (spee shee AY shun)
embryo	stabilizing selection
gene pool	vestigial structure (veh SYTIHJ ee yul)
genetic drift	

Review the definitions of the Chapter 15 vocabulary words listed in the box. Then read the statements below. If the statement is true, write *true*. If a statement is false, replace the underlined word with another vocabulary word that will make the statement true. You will not use all the words.

1. <u>Natural selection</u> is breeding living things to select for certain traits.

Artificial selection

2. <u>Mimicry</u> enables an animal or a plant to blend with its surroundings.

Camouflage

3. <u>Homologous structures</u> are similar structures found in groups of related organisms.

true

4. <u>Genetic equilibrium</u> happens when allelic frequencies stay the same from generation to generation.

true

5. The <u>allelic frequency</u> is the entire collection of genes in a population.

gene pool

Use the vocabulary words in the box below. Review the definitions of these words. Then draw a line to match each word in the box with its definition.

a. divergent evolution	6. When a physical barrier divides a population into groups
b. geographic isolation	7. Any organism that has multiple sets of chromosomes
c. convergent evolution	8. The idea that species form by gradual change over time
d. polyploid	9. When two or more similar species become more unlike each other over time
e. gradualism	10. When distantly related life forms develop similar traits

---

Chapter 16 **Primate Evolution,** *continued*

Review the Vocabulary

anthropoid (AN thruh poyd)	Neanderthals (nee AN dur tawl)
australopithecine (ah stray loh pihth uh sine)	opposable thumb
bipedal	prehensile tail (pree HEN sul)
Cro-Magnon	primate
hominid (hoh MIHN ud)	

Use some of the Chapter 16 vocabulary words listed above to fill in the puzzle.

a u s t r a l o p i t h e c i n e
n   p
t   p r i m a t e
h   o
r   s
o   a
p   b i p e d a l
o   l
i   p r e h e n s i l e
d

Across

1. early hominid that lived in Africa

3. group of mammals that includes lemurs, monkeys, apes, and humans

4. ability to walk upright on two legs

5. type of tail that can grasp tree branches

Down

1. subgroup of primates that includes monkeys, apes, and humans

2. type of thumb that can be used to grasp objects

Use the rest of the vocabulary words to finish the words in the sentences.

6. **Neanderthals** _____ lived from 35 000 to 100 000 years ago.

7. _____ **Hominids** are humanlike primates that walk on two legs.

8. _____ **Cro-** _____ **Magnon** _____ people lived in Europe 35 000 to 40 000 years ago.

Content Mastery

Chapter 18 Viruses and Bacteria, continued

Review the Vocabulary

Use the Chapter 18 vocabulary words in the box to fill in the puzzle.

virus (VI rus)	bacteriophage (bak TEER ee yuh fayj)	retrovirus
provirus	toxin	endospore

Crossword:
- 1 (down) r / e
- 2 (down) v
- 3 (across) b a c t e r i o p h a g 4 e
- r / r / n
- 5 (across) t o x i n / o / v / d
- r / u / o
- u / s / s
- 6 (across) p r o v i r u s / o
- e

Across

3. virus that infects only bacteria
5. poison produced by some bacteria
6. virus whose DNA has been inserted into the host cell's chromosome

Down

1. virus that has RNA
2. tiny, nonliving particle
4. bacterium with a tough outer covering

Look at each vocabulary word in the box below. If the word is related to bacteria, write it in the table under *Bacteria*. If the word is related to viruses, write it in the table under *Viruses*.

lytic cycle (LI tihk)
lysogenic cycle (li suh JEN ihk)
capsid
reverse transcriptase
obligate aerobe
binary fission
conjugation
obligate anaerobe
nitrogen fixation

Bacteria	Viruses
obligate aerobe	lytic cycle
obligate anaerobe	lysogenic cycle
binary fission	capsid
conjugation	reverse transcriptase
nitrogen fixation	

Content Mastery

Chapter 17 Organizing Life's Diversity, continued

Review the Vocabulary

Use the Chapter 17 vocabulary words listed in the box to fill in the blanks in the sentences. You will not use all the words.

binomial nomenclature	phylogeny (fi LAW juh nee)
cladistics	protists
division	taxonomy
eubacteria	

1. The naming system called **binomial nomenclature** gives each species a two-word name.

2. __Cladistics__ is a classification system based on the derived traits of organisms.

3. __Eubacteria__ are prokaryotes.

4. __Taxonomy__ is the branch of biology that groups and names living things.

5. __Phylogeny__ is the history of the evolution of a species.

Draw a line to match each vocabulary word in the box with its definition.

a. family
b. order
c. genus (JEE nus)
d. phylum (FI lum)
e. class
f. kingdom

6. Group of related orders
7. Group of related genera
8. Group of related species
9. Group of related families
10. Group of related phyla
11. Group of related classes

Chapter 20 Fungi, *continued*

Review the Vocabulary

Use the Chapter 20 vocabulary words in the box to fill in the puzzle. You will not use all the words.

mycorrhiza (my kuh RHY zuh)	hypha (HI fuh)
conidiophore (kuh NIH dee uh for)	sporangium (spuh RAN jee um)
haustoria (haw STOR ee uh)	mycelium (mi SEE lee um)

1. Sac or case where spores are produced **spo** r **an** g **ium**
2. Mutualistic relationship between a fungus and a plant **my** c **orr** h **iza**
3. Hyphae that grow into host cells without killing them **haus** t **oria**
4. Network of filaments **m** y **celium**
5. Basic structural unit of fungi **hy** p **ha**

Use the vocabulary words in the box below. Review the definitions of these words. Then draw a line to match each word in the box with its definition.

a. ascospore
b. ascus
c. basidia (buh SIH dee uh)
d. basidiospore
e. conidium (kuh NIH dee um)

6. Small sac in which sexual spores develop
7. Spore produced by basidia
8. Asexual spore in a chain of spores
9. Club-shaped hyphae
10. Spore produced in an ascus

Read the statements below. If the statement is true, write T on the line. If the statement is false, write F.

T **11.** A stolon (STOH lun) is a hypha that grows across a food source.

F **12.** A zygospore (ZI goh spor) is a fungal structure with a haploid nucleus.

F **13.** A rhizoid (RI zoyd) is a fungus that has a symbiotic relationship with green algae.

F **14.** Lichens (LI kunz) are club-shaped hyphae.

T **15.** A gametangium (gam uh TAN jee um) is a fungal structure with a haploid nucleus.

Chapter 19 Protists, *continued*

Review the Vocabulary

Use the Chapter 19 vocabulary words in the box below to fill in the blanks in the sentences. You will not use all the words.

algae (AL jee)	ciliate
flagellate (FLAJ uh lut)	plasmodium (plaz MOH dee um)
pseudopodia (sew duh POH dee uh)	protozoan (proh tuh ZOH un)
sporozoan (spor uh ZOH un)	

1. An animal-like protist is called a(n) **protozoan** .
2. An animal-like protist that has flagella is called a(n) **flagellate** .
3. A(n) **sporozoan** is a protist that produces spores.
4. Some protists use **pseudopodia** to move and to capture food.
5. A(n) **ciliate** is a protist that has cilia.

Use the vocabulary words in the box below. Review the definitions of these words. Then draw a line to match each word in the box with its definition.

a. alternation of generations
b. colony (KAH luh nee)
c. gametophyte (guh MEE tuh fite)
d. sporophyte (SPOR uh fite)
e. thallus (THAL us)

1. Haploid form of algae that produces sex cells
2. Algal body without roots, stems, or leaves
3. Group of cells that live together
4. Diploid form of algae that produces spores
5. Life cycle of algae that have a haploid stage followed by a diploid stage

Chapter 21 · What Is a Plant?, *continued*

Review the Vocabulary

Use the Chapter 21 vocabulary words in the box to label the parts of the plant.

cuticle (KYEW tih kul)
leaf
root
seed
stem

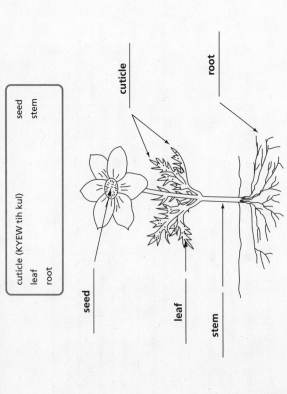

seed

cuticle

leaf

stem

root

Look at the vocabulary statements below. If the statement is true, write T on the line. If the statement is false, write F.

F 1. Nonvascular plants possess vascular tissues.

T 2. A **frond** is the leaf found on ferns that vary in length from 1 cm to 500 cm.

T 3. Tubelike, elongated cells through which water, food, and other materials are transported make up **vascular tissues.**

F 4. **Cuticles** are scaly structures that support male or female reproductive structures.

T 5. Plants that possess vascular tissues are known as **vascular plants.**

Chapter 22 · The Diversity of Plants, *continued*

Review the Vocabulary

archegonium
antheridium
cotyledon (kah tuh LEE dun)
deciduous plant (dih SIH juh wus)
dicotyledon
fruit
frond (FRAWND)
monocotyledon
perennial
prothallus
rhizome (RI zohm)
sorus (SOR us)

Use the Chapter 22 vocabulary words listed above to fill in the blanks in the statements.

1. A fern leaf is called a ___**frond**___ .

2. A(n) ___**monocotyledon**___ has one seed leaf, leaves with parallel veins, and flower parts in multiples of three.

3. A plant that lives for several years is called a(n) ___**perennial**___ . It produces flowers and seeds periodically, usually once a year.

4. A(n) ___**dicotyledon**___ has two seed leaves, leaves with branched veins, and flower parts in multiples of four or five.

5. A(n) ___**deciduous plant**___ loses all its leaves at one time.

6. The part of the seed plant embryo that functions to store food is the ___**cotyledon**___ .

7. The thick underground stem in ferns is the ___**rhizome**___ .

8. A(n) ___**antheridium**___ is a male reproductive structure in which sperm are produced.

9. The spores released from a strobilus then grow to form a gametophyte, called a(n) ___**prothallus**___ .

10. A group of sporangia on the back of a fern frond is called a(n) ___**sorus**___ .

11. A(n) ___**fruit**___ is the ripened ovary of a flower.

12. The female reproductive structure in which eggs are produced is called a(n) ___**archegonium**___ .

Chapter 23   Plant Structure and Function, *continued*

Review the Vocabulary

cortex   petiole (PET ee ohl)
epidermis   phloem (FLOH em)
guard cells   transpiration
parenchyma (puh RENG kuh muh)   tropism (TROH pih zum)
pericycle   xylem (ZI lum)

Review the Chapter 23 vocabulary words listed in the box. Then write the correct word on the line after each definition below.

1. Tissue that transports water and minerals from roots to the rest of the plant   **xylem**

2. Thin-walled cells often used for storage   **parenchyma**

3. Cells in leaf epidermis that control the opening and closing of stomatal pores   **guard cells**

4. Leaf part that joins the leaf to the stem   **petiole**

5. A plant's response to an external stimuli that causes a growth response   **tropism**

6. Outermost layer of cells in plants   **epidermis**

7. Plant tissue that helps form lateral roots   **pericycle**

8. Tissue found in plant stems and roots between the epidermis and vascular core   **cortex**

9. Evaporation of water from the stomata of leaves   **transpiration**

10. Tissue that transports sugar from the leaves to all parts of the plant   **phloem**

Chapter 24   Reproduction in Plants, *continued*

Review the Vocabulary

anther   ovary
dormancy   petal
endosperm   photoperiodism
germination   short-day plant
long-day plant   stamen
micropyle (MI kruh pile)

Review the Chapter 24 vocabulary words listed in the box. Then write the correct word on the line after each definition below.

1. Plant's response to the difference in day and night length   **photoperiodism**

2. Flower parts that are usually brightly colored and leaflike   **petals**

3. Process by which a seed begins to develop into a new plant   **germination**

4. Period of seed inactivity   **dormancy**

5. Tiny opening in the ovule through which sperm enter   **micropyle**

6. Plant that flowers when exposed to a long night   **short-day plant**

7. Food-storage tissue used by developing anthophyte embryo   **endosperm**

8. Female reproductive organ formed at lower end of pistil   **ovary**

9. Consists of an anther and a filament   **stamen**

10. Plant that flowers when the nights are short   **long-day plant**

11. Male reproductive structure that contains pollen grains   **anther**

Content Mastery

Chapter 25

What Is an Animal?, continued

Review the Vocabulary

Circle the Chapter 25 vocabulary word in brackets that best matches each description.

1. A sponge is an example of a(n) _____ organism.
[sessile (SES sile) / dorsal / ventral / anterior]

2. hollow ball made up of a single layer of cells
[gastrula (GAS truh luh) / deuterostome (DEW tuh roh stohm) / blastula / coelom]

3. layer of cells on the outer surface of the gastrula
[ectoderm / endoderm / mesoderm / exoskeleton]

4. An earthworm is an example of a(n) _____ .
[acoelomate / pseudocoelom / protostome / gastrula]

5. Most sponges have this type of symmetry (SIH muh tree).
[radial / bilateral / asymmetry / ventral]

6. Hydras have this type of symmetry.
[radial / bilateral / asymmetry / dorsal]

7. An organism that can be divided down its length into halves that are mirror images of each other is said to have _____ symmetry.
[radial / bilateral / ventral/ dorsal]

8. head end of a flatworm
[posterior / dorsal / ventral / anterior]

9. an animal that has three cell layers with a digestive tract but no body cavity
[pseudocoelomate / coelomate / acoelomate (uh SEE luh mayt) / protostome]

10. Humans, insects, and fishes have this type of body cavity.
[coelom (SEE lum) / pseudocoelom (sew duh SEE lum) / acoelom / gastrula]

11. An internal skeleton is called a(n) _____ .
[exoskeleton / endoskeleton / blastula / protostome (PROH tuh stohm)]

Content Mastery

Chapter 26

Sponges, Cnidarians, Flatworms, and Roundworms, continued

Review the Vocabulary

a. external fertilization

b. filter feeding

c. gastrovascular cavity (gas troh VAS kyuh lur)

d. hermaphrodite (hur MAF ruh dite)

e. internal fertilization

f. medusa

g. nematocyst (nuh MAT uh sihst)

h. nerve net

i. pharynx (FAYR ingks)

j. polyp (PAH lup)

k. proglottid (proh GLAH tud)

l. scolex (SKOH leks)

Write the letters of the Chapter 26 vocabulary words on the lines after the definitions. One word has been matched with its definition to help you get started.

1. Reproduction in which the eggs are fertilized inside the animal's body _____ e

2. Reproduction in which the eggs are fertilized outside the animal's body _____ a

3. Conducts nerve impulses in cnidarians _____ h

4. Individual, repeating sections of a tapeworm _____ k

5. The way in which sponges get their food _____ b

6. Tubelike organ used by planarians to suck food into the digestive system _____ i

7. Structure used by cnidarians to capture or poison their prey _____ g

8. Individual that can produce both eggs and sperm _____ d

9. Stage of cnidarian life cycle in which its body is shaped like a tube _____ j

10. Cavity in which cnidarian digestion takes place _____ c

11. Head of a tapeworm _____ l

12. Stage of cnidarian life cycle in which its body is shaped like an umbrella _____ f

Chapter 28 Arthropods, continued

Review the Vocabulary

appendage	chelicerae (kuh LIH sur ee)
book lungs	mandible (MAN duh bul)
compound eyes	pedipalps (PED uh palps)
larva	pheromone (FAYR uh mohn)
molting	spinnerets (sih nuh RETS)
nymph (NIHMF)	spiracles (SPEER uh kulz)
pupa	tracheal tube (TRAY kee ul)
simple eye	

Many of the Chapter 28 vocabulary words are listed in the box. Review the definitions of these words. Then fill in each blank in the sentences below with the correct word.

1. A(n) **pheromone** is an odor given off by animals.

2. The wormlike stage of an insect is the **larva** .

3. A(n) **appendage** is a structure that grows out of an animal's body.

4. Arachnids use **pedipalps** for holding food and for sensing.

5. The biting appendages of arachnids are called **chelicerae** .

6. Spiders use **spinnerets** to spin silk into thread.

7. Spiders and their relatives use **book lungs** to breathe.

8. A(n) **nymph** hatches from an egg during incomplete metamorphosis.

9. Many arthropods see with a pair of large **compound eyes** .

10. The mouthpart an arthropod uses to hold, chew, suck, or bite food is called a(n) **mandible** .

Chapter 27 Mollusks and Segmented Worms, continued

Review the Vocabulary

Use the Chapter 27 vocabulary words to fill in the puzzle.

closed circulatory system	gizzard	mantle
nephridia (ne FRIH dee uh)	open circulatory system	radula (RAJ uh luh)

ACROSS

2. Blood moves into open spaces around an animal's organs. This is called an open _____ system.

5. thin membrane that protects a mollusk's organs

6. structures that remove waste from an animal's body

DOWN

1. tonguelike organ used to scrape or cut food

3. annelid organ that grinds food

4. The blood in an animal's body stays in the blood vessels. This is called a(n) _____ circulatory system.

Content Mastery

Chapter 29   Echinoderms and Invertebrates Chordates, *continued*

Review the Vocabulary

Use the Chapter 29 vocabulary words in the box to fill in the puzzle.

ampulla (am POOL uh)
madreporite (MAD ruh por ite)
notochord (NOH tuh kord)
pedicellaria (ped uh suh LAYR ee uh)
ray

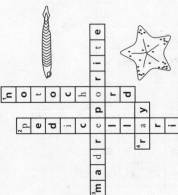

Across

3. disk-shaped opening in an echinoderm's body that lets water in and out

4. long, tapering arm of an echinoderm

5. round, muscular structure that squeezes water into or out of tube feet

Down

1. long, rodlike structure in all chordates

2. pincerlike appendage on an echinoderm

Find the vocabulary word in the box that matches each definition. Then write the letter of the word on the line in front of the definition.

___d___ **6.** System in echinoderms that helps them move, respire, eat, and get rid of waste

___c___ **7.** Hollow, thin-walled tubes with a suction cup on the end

___a___ **8.** Tube of cells surrounding a fluid-filled canal above the notochord

___b___ **9.** Paired openings located behind the mouth

a. dorsal hollow nerve cord
b. gill slits
c. tube feet
d. water vascular system

Content Mastery

Chapter 30   Fishes and Amphibians, *continued*

Review the Vocabulary

cartilage
fin
scale
swim bladder

ectotherm
lateral line system
spawning
vocal cords

Use three of the Chapter 30 vocabulary words listed above to fill in the blanks in the statements.

1. The ___lateral line system___ is a line of canals along the side of a fish that help it detect movements and find its way in the dark.

2. A(n) ___swim bladder___ is a gas-filled sac in bony fishes that helps them control their depth.

3. ___Vocal cords___ are bands of tissue in the throats of frogs and mammals. These bands enable animals to make sounds.

Use the rest of the vocabulary words to fill in the puzzle.

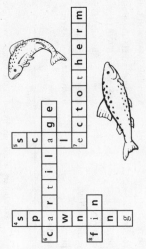

Across

6. tough, flexible material that forms the skeleton in some fishes

7. animal whose body temperature is controlled by the environment

8. fan-shaped membrane used by fishes for balance

Down

4. kind of breeding in fish and some other animals

5. one of many thin, bony plates that cover the skin of a fish

---

Chapter 31 — Reptiles and Birds, *continued*

Review the Vocabulary

endotherm   amniotic egg (am nee YAH tihk)
feather   Jacobson's organ
sternum

Use the Chapter 31 vocabulary words listed above to fill in the puzzle.

	¹a	m	n	i	o	t	i	c
²f								
e					o			
J	a	c	o	b	s	o	n	'	s
t					e	n	d	o	t	h	e	r	m
h					r			
e					n			
r				⁴s	u			
			³s	t	m			

Across

3. Reptiles use their _____ organ to detect chemicals in the air.

5. animal that maintains a constant body temperature even if the temperature of its environment changes

Down

1. kind of egg that has a shell and fluid to protect the embryo

2. lightweight, modified scale that provides insulation for birds and allows them to fly

4. breastbone

Chapter 32 — Mammals, *continued*

Review the Vocabulary

Use the Chapter 32 vocabulary words in the box to fill in the blanks below.

gestation (jes TAY shun)   mammary gland
marsupial   placenta
placental mammal   uterus (YEW tuh rus)

1. Muscular, hollow organ in which offspring develop   __u__ t __erus__

2. Type of mammal that carries its young inside the uterus until development is nearly
complete   **pl** a **cental mam** m **al**

3. Time during which young mammals develop in the uterus   **ge** s **tation**

4. Organ that develops during pregnancy, provides food and oxygen to the embryo, and removes
wastes   **p** l **ac** e **nta**

5. Gland in female mammals that produces milk for the young   **ma** m **m** a **ry**

6. A kangaroo is a   **m** a **rs** u **pial**

Draw a line to match each vocabulary word in the box with its definition.

a. diaphragm (DI uh fram)
b. gland
c. monotreme (MAH nuh treem)
d. therapsid (thuh RAP sud)

7. Egg-laying mammal

8. Mammal-like reptile ancestor of all mammals

9. Sheet of muscle under the chest cavity that helps
mammals breathe

10. Group of cells that secrete substances needed by
an animal

Content Mastery

Chapter 34 Protection, Support, and Locomotion, *continued*

Review the Vocabulary

Use the Chapter 34 vocabulary words in the box to complete the spelling of the word defined to the left. You will not use all the words.

| dermis (DUR mus) | epidermis | hair follicle |
| keratin (KAYR uh tun) | melanin (MEL uh nun) | myosin (MI uh sun) |

1. thin, outer layer of skin **epi** d **ermis**

2. protein in dead epidermal cells **ker** at **in**

3. cell pigment that colors the skin and protects it from sun damage **m** el **anin**

4. thick, inner layer of skin **derm** is

5. small cavity in the dermis that grows hair h **air** f **ollicle**

Review the definitions of the underlined vocabulary words in the statements below. If the statement is true, write true. If the statement is false, replace the underlined word with another vocabulary word that will make the statement true.

6. The axial skeleton includes the bones of the arms and legs. **appendicular skeleton**

7. A knee is an example of a joint. **true**

8. A ligament is a thick band of tissue that attaches muscles to bone. **tendon**

9. Bursae (BUR sigh) are fluid-filled sacs in joints. **true**

10. A potential bone cell is called an osteoblast (AH stee uh blast). **true**

11. Compact bone has many holes and spaces. **spongy bone**

12. Marrow is the soft tissue inside of bones. **true**

13. Smooth muscle is found in the heart. **cardiac muscle**

14. Skeletal muscle is attached to bones and moves the skeleton. **true**

15. Involuntary muscle contracts when you try to contract it. **voluntary muscle**

16. A small fiber that makes up larger muscle fibers is called a myofibril (mi yuh FI brul). **true**

17. Thick filaments in myofibrils are made of the protein actin. **myosin**

18. Each section of a myofibril is called a sarcomere (SAR koh meer). **true**

19. The sliding filament theory states that actin filaments slide together during muscle contraction. **true**

Content Mastery

Chapter 33 Animal Behavior, *continued*

Review the Vocabulary

Review the definitions of the Chapter 33 vocabulary words in bold type in the statements below. If the statement is true, write true. If the statement is false, write false.

false 1. An instinct is anything an animal does in response to a stimulus in the environment.

true 2. Innate behavior is inherited behavior.

true 3. Courtship behavior takes place before male and female animals mate.

false 4. Aggressive behavior is not threatening to other animals.

true 5. A territory is a physical space where animals breed, feed, or get shelter.

true 6. The fight-or-flight response prepares the body for greater activity.

false 7. Animals that live in very cold climates experience estivation (es tuh VAY shun).

true 8. A 24-hour cycle of behavior is called a circadian (sur KAY dee un) rhythm.

false 9. During hibernation, animals have a great need for oxygen and energy.

true 10. A dominance hierarchy is a social order with several levels.

Draw a line to match each word in the box with its definition.

a. communication
b. conditioning
c. habituation (huh bih chuh WAY shun)
d. imprinting
e. insight
f. language
g. motivation
h. trial-and-error learning

11. Internal need that causes an animal to act

12. Occurs when an animal is given a stimulus without punishment or reward

13. Attachment to an object during a certain time in an animal's life

14. Kind of learning in which an animal is rewarded for a particular response

15. kind of learning in which an animal uses its experience to respond to something new

16. kind of learning in which an animal connects a new stimulus to a certain behavior

17. Using symbols to represent ideas

18. Sharing of information that results in a change of behavior

Content Mastery

Chapter 36   The Nervous System, *continued*

Review the Vocabulary

addiction	nervous system	cerebellum
cerebrum	cochlea	retina
neuron (NEW rahn)	reflex	taste bud
rods	withdrawal	synapse (SIH naps)

```
f r a x e d h l u c e n
c e r e b e l l u m t e
e w i t h d r a w a l r
r n l d j h e d m l c v
e e g f i o f d r k o o
b u t e e e c t g h u
r r u i e e x l h s
u o e m n e c g s j
m n s h d a s i a e y
m a c w v e r o d s y
r g s y h e b n s d t
t a s t e b u d f a e
w f s a y n a p s e m
a d e b n l g i w n e q
```

Use the Chapter 36 vocabulary words listed above to complete the puzzle. First, write the correct word on the line after each definition. Then find the same word in the letter grid and circle it. Words may be written on horizontal, vertical, or diagonal lines.

1. Psychological or physiological drug dependence   **addiction**

2. Layer of the eye containing rods and cones   **retina**

3. Body's control center   **nervous system**

4. Taste receptor on tongue   **taste bud**

5. Portion of brain that maintains balance and muscle coordination   **cerebellum**

6. Psychological or physiological illness resulting from cessation of drug use   **withdrawal**

7. Largest portion of the brain   **cerebrum**

8. Place where neurons meet   **synapse**

9. Fluid-filled structure of the ear in which sound vibrations are converted into nerve impulses   **cochlea**

10. Light receptors in the retina responsible for vision in low light   **rods**

11. Basic structural and functional unit in the nervous system   **neuron**

12. Rapid, automatic response to a stimulus   **reflex**

Content Mastery

Chapter 35   The Digestive and Endocrine Systems, *continued*

Review the Vocabulary

amylase (AM uh lays)	pancreas (PANG kree us)
bile	peristalsis (payr uh STAWL sus)
pituitary	small intestine
endocrine	stomach
gallbladder	villus (VIH lus)
negative feedback	vitamin (VI tuh mun)

Use the Chapter 35 vocabulary words in the box to fill in the blanks in the sentences.

1. The pouchlike, muscular organ that secretes acids and digestive enzymes is the **stomach**.

2. **Bile** is a chemical produced by the liver that helps break down fats.

3. The endocrine system is regulated by a **negative feedback** system.

4. **Amylase** is a digestive enzyme that breaks starches into sugars.

5. The **pituitary** gland controls many other glands of the endocrine system.

6. **Peristalsis** is a wave of muscular contractions that moves food through the digestive system.

7. The organ that stores bile is the **gallbladder**.

8. A **villus** is a fingerlike projection in the lining of the small intestine.

9. The gland that produces both hormones and digestive enzymes is the **pancreas**.

10. Digestion is completed in the organ called the **small intestine**.

11. A **vitamin** is an organic substance that regulates body processes.

12. **Endocrine** glands release hormones directly into the bloodstream.

Content Mastery

Chapter 37   Respiration, Circulation, and Excretion, *continued*

Review the Vocabulary

alveoli (al VEE uh li)
aorta
artery
atrium
hemoglobin (HEE muh gloh bun)
kidneys

nephron (NE frawn)
plasma
pulse
ureter (YUR uh tur)
vein

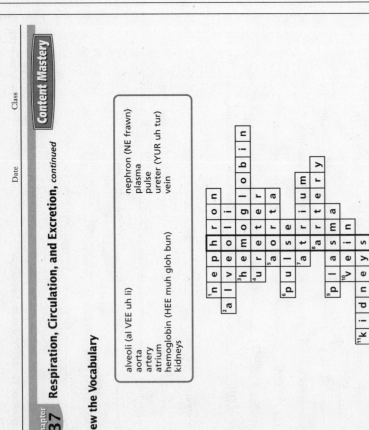

Review the definitions of the Chapter 37 vocabulary words listed above. Then use the clues to complete the puzzle. The letters in the dark boxes will make up a word that means the process by which the body balances nutrients and other things it needs for life.

1. filtering unit of the kidney
2. tiny, thin-walled sacs in the lungs
3. iron-containing molecule of red blood cells
4. tube that transports urine from each kidney to the urinary bladder
5. largest blood vessel in the human body
6. rhythmic surge of blood through an artery
7. thin-walled upper chambers of the heart
8. thick-walled blood vessel that transports blood away from the heart
9. fluid portion of the blood
10. large blood vessel that returns blood from the tissues back to the heart
11. pair of organs that filter waste from blood

Content Mastery

Chapter 38   Reproduction and Development, *continued*

Review the Vocabulary

a. first trimester
b. cervix
c. epididymis (ep uh DIHD uh mus)
d. follicle (FAH lih kul)
e. implantation
f. labor
g. ovulation
h. puberty
i. scrotum
j. seminal vesicles
k. vas deferens (vas • DEF uh runtz)

Write the letter of the Chapter 38 vocabulary words in the box in front of their definitions.

__d__ 1. Group of epithelial cells that surround a developing egg in the ovary

__a__ 2. First part of pregnancy when all the organ systems of the embryo begin to form

__i__ 3. Testes-containing sac of males

__b__ 4. Lower end of the uterus that opens into the vagina

__h__ 5. Growth stage that occurs in both males and females, characterized by the development of secondary sex characteristics

__c__ 6. Single-coiled tube in which sperm complete maturation

__k__ 7. Duct through which sperm move from the epididymis toward the urethra

__g__ 8. Process in which the follicle ruptures to release the egg from the ovary

__e__ 9. Attachment of the fertilized egg to the uterine lining

__f__ 10. Physical and psychological changes that the mother experiences during birth

__j__ 11. Paired glands at the base of the urinary bladder that produce fluid to nourish sperm

Chapter 39 Immunity from Disease, continued

Content Mastery

Review the Vocabulary

antibiotic	Koch's postulates
B cell	(KAHKS • PAHS chuh lutz)
interferon	lymph (LIHMF)
endemic disease	lymph node
epidemic	lymphocyte
immunity	(LIHMF uh site)
(ihm YEW nut ee)	macrophage
infectious disease	(MAK ruh fayj)
	pathogen (PATH uh jun)
	phagocyte (FAG uh site)
	pus
	T cell
	tissue fluid
	vaccine (vak SEEN)
	virus

For each statement below, circle the Chapter 39 vocabulary word inside the brackets that best completes the statement. You will not use every word.

1. Diseases are caused by the presence of [oxygen / antibiotics / **a pathogen** / alleles] in the body.

2. During a(n) [antibiotic / **epidemic** / genetic disorder / abnormality], many people have the same disease at the same time.

3. Penicillin is an example of a(n) [**antibiotic** / pathogen / endemic disease / lymphocyte].

4. The fluid in the lymphatic system is called [pus / blood / salt water / **lymph**].

5. A [lymphocyte / **virus** / phagocyte / macrophage] is *not* a white blood cell that protects the body against foreign substances.

6. The [**B cell** / C cell / D cell / F cell] is a type of lymphocyte.

7. [Pus / Skin / Mucus / **A vaccine**] can cause immunity to a disease.

8. Chicken pox, tetanus, tuberculosis, and AIDS are all [reproductive disorders / genetic disorders / **infectious diseases** / environmental diseases].

9. A disease that is continually present in the population is called a(n) [**endemic disease** / epidemic / plague / abnormality].

10. Lymph is filtered in the [**lymph nodes** / heart / brain / stomach].

11. When [calcium / carbon dioxide / blood / **tissue fluid**] enters the lymphatic vessels, it is called lymph.

12. The collection of dead white blood cells and different body fluids that are found around an infected area is called [an antibiotic / **pus** / complement / a vaccine].

CONTENT MASTERY